ALONG LAUGHING BROOK

ALONG
LAUGHING BROOK

A Book of Nature Stories by
THORNTON W. BURGESS

Illustrated by
HARRISON CADY

LITTLE, BROWN AND COMPANY
BOSTON · 1949

jBg12al

*Published simultaneously
in Canada by McClelland and Stewart Limited*

PRINTED IN THE UNITED STATES OF AMERICA

Contents

ALONG LAUGHING BROOK

I. Along Laughing Brook

A bit of knowledge gained each day
In time to wisdom points the way.
— OLD MOTHER NATURE

FAR UP ON THE GREAT MOUNTAIN, a tiny stream, Laughing Brook, begins its long journey to join the distant Big River and go with it on and on and on to the Vast Ocean. At first it is without sound, trickling over smooth rock. Then in the joy of its freedom to choose its own way it chuckles softly, a silvery chuckle that only the quick ears of little woodland folk who happen near may hear. In that sound is pure delight as if the streamlet has foreknowledge of where it is going and all the wonderful things and exciting things and beautiful things it will see and experience along the way.

From time to time other streamlets join it and Laughing Brook widens and begins to hurry, and the sound of it is the sound of laughter. It falls over ledges to splash happily in little moss-girt pools. It chooses its own winding way down through the Green Forest, racing noisily over small stones and around big ones; loafing under great trees in deep, dark pools the trout love; lazily sunning itself in ponds wherein Paddy the Beaver has trapped it; flowing gently in deep contentment between higher banks through the low land, and so to the Smiling Pool on the Green Meadows and on to the Big River.

In the icy clasp of winter it gurgles sleepily. In spring it rushes headlong in boisterous tumult. In summer and fall it idles restfully.

Laughing Brook is beloved by many folk in fur and feathers and some in neither. Some come to it daily or nightly to drink or bathe. Some, like Little Joe Otter and Billy Mink, travel up and down its length to fish. Some make their homes in it, beside it or near it. In its long journey Laughing Brook sees love, anger, happiness, sorrow, adventure, danger, fright, anxiety, bravery, contentment, thrift, wastefulness, courage — all that goes to make up life. And in it all it has a part.

Peter Rabbit loves to visit Laughing Brook and often does, especially where it makes its way through the little swamp at the head of the Smiling Pool. Long ago he learned that a swamp is one of the best places in which to look for the first signs of the return of sweet Mistress Spring. Peter was over in that little swamp just poking about. He sat up and his wobbly little nose began to twitch. A familiar smell tickled it.

"Jimmy Skunk has been around here," said he to himself as he sat up and sniffed. "Yes, sir, he has been around here. I wonder if he is around now. I would like to see him. I haven't seen him since last fall. I heard that he was out two or three times in the winter during mild spells, but I didn't see him. I wonder if I can find him."

So Peter began looking around for Jimmy Skunk. He first made sure of the direction from which the Merry Little Breezes were bringing that pleasantly unpleasant odor.

"It is funny about that smell," thought he as he sniffed. "A lot of it is terrible. Yes, sir, it is terrible. I don't know of any worse smell. But a little of it like this is not bad at all. In fact I rather like it. I wonder what Jimmy is doing down here. The last I knew he was living over near the Old Pasture. Perhaps he got spring fever and itching heels like me."

He wandered all through that little swamp but he didn't find Jimmy Skunk. Sometimes he would lose that smell altogether. Again it would be so strong that he would look all around expectantly, but no Jimmy Skunk. At last he found a place where the smell was particularly strong, though not unpleasantly so. Once more he sat up to look this way and that way. Right in front of him was a very wet place. On part of it there was a little water. Peter happened to look down at it. At the very edge of the water was a curious-looking thing, dark reddish-brown

5

streaked with green. It was shaped like a hood, the kind that monks of long ago used to wear, called a cowl.

You should have seen the foolish look on Peter's face. He knew what that curious hood was. It was part of a plant, and it was from this that that smell was coming.

"Skunk cabbage!" exclaimed Peter. "Of course. Why didn't I think of that before?"

It was a funny mistake, but a happy one for now Peter knew for certain that Mistress Spring was not far away. He was startled by a voice behind him. He turned quickly to find his big cousin, Jumper the Hare, still wearing his white winter coat.

"Do you smell anything?" asked Peter, twitching his wobbly little nose.

Jumper sat up and sniffed. Then he made a face. "Now you speak of it, I do. I smell Jimmy Skunk, and I don't like it," said he.

"I don't smell Jimmy Skunk, but I do smell proof that Mistress Spring isn't far away, and I like it," said Peter. He stepped aside.

Then Jumper saw what Peter had found and knew at once what it was. His eyes brightened. He sniffed again. "So that's it! Smells good, doesn't it?" said he.

"I thought you didn't like it," Peter reminded him.

Jumper paid no attention to this. "Yes, sir, it surely does smell good, for it is the first real spring smell," he continued. "In the Green Forest there is still snow in places. Jack Frost is still hang-

ing around and nights are cold. But smelling that skunk cabbage makes a fellow forget those things. As I live, Peter, there is Busy Bee! Even though it is fairly warm in the sun I didn't expect to see her out. What do you suppose has brought her over here? I don't see what she is out for anyway; there are no flowers yet."

Busy Bee buzzed about that odd hood at the water's edge. Then she disappeared. Through a narrow opening on the inside of that curved hood she had crawled inside. Peter and Jumper stared in surprise.

"What do you suppose she went in there for?" asked Peter.

Jumper shook his head. "Don't ask me. I haven't the least idea," said he.

They continued to stare. After a while Busy Bee crawled out. She saw Jumper and Peter. "It is nice to have flowers in bloom again, isn't it? I certainly am glad to get some fresh pollen," she buzzed in their long ears, then flew away. She left them blinking.

"What did she mean? There are no flowers around here. What is more, there won't be for some time," said Jumper.

"Did you notice that yellow stuff she had?" Peter asked.

His big cousin admitted that he did, but he didn't know what it was. Peter moved to where he could peep into the hood through the narrow opening. There was an odd expression on his face as he turned to look up at Jumper. "It's in here. She got it in here," said he.

"What's in there? What are you talking about?" Jumper wanted to know.

"That yellow dust," replied Peter.

Jumper peeped in. "You are right, Cousin Peter. This is where she got it sure enough. I wonder if that is the pollen she spoke of," said he.

Peter made an excited little hop. "Of course!" he cried. "And you find it only in flowers. So you know what that means?"

"What does it mean?" asked his cousin.

"Why, it means that there must be flowers inside there. That smell must come from them. It means that we have found the very first flowers of the year, and Mistress Spring must be just around the corner," cried Peter happily.

Peter was right. Inside that thick fleshy hood, protecting them and keeping them snug and warm, were tiny blossoms called florets. But tiny as they were they produced the yellow dust called pollen. Later, when the tiny flowers had gone, there would be big, broad green leaves, as big as cabbage leaves. So some folks call the plant the swamp cabbage, but most folks call it skunk cabbage because of the smell. And Jimmy Skunk has nothing to do with it.

A week or two later the smell was much stronger for now there were many of these quaint plants. Peter found some of the oldest of these crowded with tiny Flies although the weather was still cold and nights frosty.

9

"It is wonderful. Yes, sir, it is wonderful," declared Peter admiringly.

"What is wonderful?" asked Redwing the Blackbird, who had arrived that very morning.

"That those teeny weeny Flies can live in such cold weather," said Peter.

"They lived all winter, so why shouldn't they live now?" replied Redwing.

"They did not," declared Peter. "I was over here often in the winter and if any had been flying about I would have seen them. So there!"

"I didn't say they were flying about. I guess they didn't have wings and didn't look like Flies any more than a Butterfly asleep for the winter looks like a Butterfly, but they were alive just the same," replied Redwing good-naturedly.

"Where were they?" demanded Peter.

"I don't know for sure, but I guess they were in moss, or under leaves, on the ground," replied Redwing. That was a very good guess. They had wakened now to aid Mother Nature by carrying grains of pollen from plant to plant as they swarmed in and out of the odd little hoods that protected the tiny flowers and their tiny selves. Truly it was wonderful, as Peter said.

II. Peter Looks for Longbill

Be careful never to intrude,
For there is nothing quite so rude.
— OLD MOTHER NATURE

IT WAS SHADOW TIME. Peter Rabbit was just leaving the dear Old Briar-patch. Mrs. Peter saw him. "Where are you going?" she demanded sharply.

"Oh, just looking," replied Peter.

Mrs. Peter stamped with vexation. "One of these times you will look once too often," she declared.

Peter said nothing. He started off, lipperty-lipperty-lip, across the Green Meadows toward the little swamp at the head of the Smiling Pool. Mrs. Peter sighed as she watched him. She reached for a leaf of clover and took it back to eat in the safe Old

11

Briar-patch. She never has understood why Peter isn't content to stay where he knows he is safe.

Peter spent the night wandering about near the Smiling Pool and for a little way along Laughing Brook. Morning found him in the little swamp through which Laughing Brook makes its way to enter the Smiling Pool.

"Now that I am here I may as well stay. Anyway, it isn't safe to cross the Green Meadows in broad daylight. Mrs. Peter wouldn't want me to try it," said Peter to himself. Of course this was just an excuse for staying.

The ground was damp and soft as is the way with ground in swampy places. Slowly and aimlessly he hopped along. He was disappointed that he had found no one with whom to gossip. All through the night he had heard some of his friends singing, but they were out in the Smiling Pool and too busy singing to come ashore to gossip. They were Hylas, the tiny Tree Frogs that most people call Peepers.

A small round hole in the soft earth caught Peter's attention. It was such a hole as you might make by pushing a slender pencil down in the ground. His first thought was that an Angleworm had made that hole, coming out to crawl about on the surface as Angleworms sometimes do at night. Then he saw another hole and presently a third. At sight of that third hole Peter's memory awakened.

"Longbill the Woodcock, or Mrs. Longbill!" he exclaimed, and at once began looking for more holes. He found a number of them. "Yes, sir, the Longbills made those holes. They have been here getting Worms. I had forgotten all about them. They always get here early. I wonder where they are now. I would like to see Longbill. I would so. And Mrs. Longbill too," said he, still talking to himself.

Now of course the whereabouts of Mr. and Mrs. Longbill was no business of Peter's. Certainly not. But people with no matters of their own to keep them busy, no duties to attend to, often try to poke their noses into the affairs of other folks. Peter, I am sorry to say, is inclined that way. He wanted to see the Longbills, but not for any particular purpose. He just wanted to see them, that was all. It didn't enter his head that they might not want to see him. Not that this would have made any difference had he thought of it. It wouldn't have.

He heard Little Friend the Song Sparrow singing over near the edge of the swamp. It was a lovely, tinkling, happy song, but Peter didn't stop to enjoy it. He was in too much of a hurry. He scampered over there as fast as his long heels could take him. He could hardly wait for greetings before asking if Little Friend had seen the Longbills.

Little Friend looked at Peter suspiciously. "Why do you want to know?" he asked.

"I have just found some holes in the ground that I am sure were made by one of them, or perhaps both. It reminded me of them and that I haven't seen so much as a feather of either of them this spring. I would like to see them and pay them a call," explained Peter.

"Have you thought that perhaps they might not like to have you pay them a call?" asked Little Friend.

Peter blinked. He looked as if he didn't understand that remark at all. "Why shouldn't they want me to pay them a call? You know very well I wouldn't hurt them. They know it too. We are old friends. Why shouldn't they be as glad to see me as I will be to see them?" Peter sounded hurt.

"They probably have seen you already, and if they wanted you

14

to see them they would have shown themselves. You know, Peter, there are times when folks enjoy most seeing others, even old friends, at a distance."

"I don't see why," said Peter.

Now if Little Friend meant that for a hint that Peter might not be altogether welcome in that neighborhood, and it certainly sounded like it, Peter didn't take it. He isn't sensitive that way. A lot of people are like him. They seem not to know what a hint is.

Peter is happy-go-lucky. You know that. Whatever he does is done in a happy-go-lucky manner. It was just so now. He merely wandered about trusting to luck that he might happen to find Longbill or Mrs. Longbill. More than ever he was sure that at least one of them was about for he had found more of the little holes in the earth. He was sure that only a Woodcock could have bored such holes as these.

"Maybe Longbill isn't staying here. Maybe he has just visited here and has gone off. If he has maybe he will come back soon," thought Peter.

Just then he heard a whistling sound behind him. He turned just in time to catch a glimpse of a brownish bird disappearing among the alders along Laughing Brook.

He kicked up his long heels as only Peter can, and away he went, lipperty-lipperty-lip, among the alders along Laughing Brook. "That was Longbill! I know it was! None but a Woodcock flies just that way," thought Peter happily.

He had gone but a little way when again he heard that whistle and again he had just a provoking glimpse of a brown bird. He tried to run faster but couldn't because there were too many bushes to dodge around. It was discouraging as well as provoking.

"What is the matter with him anyway? He knows he has nothing to fear from me. The way he acts one might think I was Reddy Fox, or Billy Mink, or someone else with a liking for a bird dinner now and then," muttered Peter.

He stopped running for he no longer knew in which direction to run. For a few minutes he sat still just looking and listening. Then once more he began moving about aimlessly, this way and that. He rounded a little clump of young birch trees and stopped abruptly. There, right in front of him, walking along sedately, was Longbill. Yes, sir, there was his old friend with the long bill and the shoe-button eyes that seem to be almost on top of his head. Longbill stopped. He put his head near the ground as if listening. Then he plunged his long bill in the ground, which was damp and soft. He drew out a Worm and swallowed it.

Peter's curiosity was so great that he didn't even say hello. What he did say was, "How did you know that Worm was down in the ground just there?"

Longbill pretended not to have heard Peter's question. "Hello, Peter!" he exclaimed just as if he had no idea at all that Peter was in the neighborhood. "It is a long time since we last met. How are you this spring? You're looking fine."

"I'm feeling fine, thank you. I've been looking for you. When did you get back here?" replied Peter. He had forgotten his previous question.

"Oh, we've been here for some time," replied Longbill.

"Did you say we?" asked Peter.

"That's what I said," replied Longbill. "The fact is Mrs. Longbill and I arrived a bit early this year so as to have time to look around thoroughly before nesting."

"I haven't seen you anywhere," protested Peter. There was a hint of doubt in his voice as if he didn't quite believe Longbill.

Longbill chuckled. "Haven't you?" said he.

"No. And I've been over here often," retorted Peter.

Again Longbill chuckled. "I'll say you have. I've seen you, and so has Mrs. Longbill. She mentioned it the other day," said he.

"Where is Mrs. Longbill?" cried Peter, looking all about as if he expected to see her right there somewhere.

"Oh, she's at home," said Longbill in a matter-of-fact tone.

Peter looked at him sharply. "Home? Did you say home?" he asked.

"Yes," replied Longbill. "She is pretty busy these days."

"Doing what?" Peter demanded.

"Sitting still," said Longbill. Peter looked at him suspiciously. Had Longbill chuckled?

III. The Song in the Sky

A song finds echo in your heart
And gloom and discontent depart.

— PETER RABBIT

PETER HAD JUST HAD a narrow escape. No one else knew it, but he did. He was safe now in the little alder thicket at the head of the Smiling Pool, but a moment before he had been outside, right out in the open. In the dusk of early evening Jerry Muskrat had seen Hooty the Owl and had slapped the water with his tail. Peter had bounded into that thicket without waiting to even find out what the danger was.

Peeper the Hyla and his friends, the tiny Tree Frogs who in early spring form the mighty chorus of the Smiling Pool,

18

stopped singing the instant Jerry's tail hit the water. It was very still, a soft stillness that could be pleasantly felt. Peter sat with his long ears set to catch the first notes from the water that would start the happy chorus again. Instead he heard faintly but clearly a song that he did not remember ever having heard before.

It was a lovely little song, a song filled with sweet mystery and love and the joy of living. Just where that song had come from Peter couldn't decide. He turned his head to one side the better to listen. He turned it to the other side. The song had stopped. For a minute or more there was no sound. Then from back of Peter over near Laughing Brook came clearly whistled notes. They seemed to be rising, going up, up, up. When they ceased Peter heard the beginning of that lovely mysterious song of a few minutes before. Then the chorus of the Hylas was resumed. It seemed as if each tiny singer must be trying his best to make up for lost time. That great chorus drowned out completely the song of which he had heard only the beginning.

For some time Peter sat right there. Once or twice he thought he heard those rising whistling notes, but he couldn't be sure. All he could be sure he heard was that chorus of the Hylas. He became impatient. He gets that way sometimes. Because he was impatient he thumped the ground hard with his hind feet. The singing in the Smiling Pool stopped abruptly. Peter chuckled.

Once more there was stillness that could almost be felt. Then Peter heard again those clearly whistled notes going up, up, up. They ended and at once were followed by that lovely unknown song. This time Peter heard it through and he was sure he knew where it came from.

"It came dropping down from way, way up in the sky," he told Mrs. Peter later when he was back in the dear Old Briar-patch.

"Pooh!" said little Mrs. Peter scornfully. "You were just hearing things. If you stayed here at home where you belong you wouldn't hear songs in the sky, not after dark anyway. Probably that singer, whoever he was, wasn't up in the sky at all. That is, if you really heard one. Probably he was in the top of a tall tree. You wouldn't know the difference."

"There are no tall trees there," retorted Peter.

"Then it must have been someone traveling at night and singing as he flew," declared Mrs. Peter.

"My dear, have you ever heard one of the feathered folks sing, really sing, when flying over at night?" Peter asked.

Mrs. Peter had to admit that she hadn't. "But I've often heard them call," she added.

"Oh that! Of course you have. So have I times without number. But calling to one another isn't singing," replied Peter scornfully, and added, "What I heard was a song, a real song. Whoever the singer was he can really sing. I think it was a love song."

"None of the Thrush family has arrived yet," said Mrs. Peter.

Peter stared at her with a puzzled look. "I didn't say that any have. What in the world have the Thrushes to do with the subject?" said he.

20

"They sing after dark," replied Mrs. Peter simply. "Who else have you heard singing after dark?"

"Whitethroat the Sparrow and Mocker the Mockingbird," was Peter's prompt reply.

Mrs. Peter looked a bit rueful. "I had forgotten them," she admitted.

"But you never have heard either singing way up in the sky. They don't sing while they are flying," cried Peter triumphantly.

"Bubbling Bob the Bobolink sings in the air," asserted Mrs. Peter.

"He isn't here yet. Besides, he doesn't sing in the night," retorted Peter.

All this served only to increase Peter's curiosity regarding the mysterious singer in the evening sky. He asked all his feathered friends who happened to drop into the Old Briar-patch if they knew the mysterious singer. None did. They hadn't heard that song. Most, if not all of them, have retired for the night by the time the Black Shadows from the Purple Hills reach the Smiling Pool and the alder thicket at its head.

Wherever he was at night Peter kept his ears open for that lovely mysterious song. He listened in the Old Pasture. He listened in the Old Orchard. He listened in the Green Forest. Nowhere did he hear even a note of that lovely song until once more in the dusk of a quiet evening he was back near Laughing Brook in the alder thicket. There, when the Smiling Pool chorus had been alarmed into stillness, he heard again that lovely little song dropping down out of the sky. Then as before the chorus of the Hylas drowned it out.

Peter took to spending much of his time in the little swamp of which the alder thicket was a part. In the daytime Redwing the Blackbird did a lot of singing there. He had arrived early and now Mrs. Redwing was there also and Redwing sang to her much of the time from dawn to dark.

Peter listened to that song hoping that in it he might hear some familiar notes, the ones that had come tumbling down to him through the evening dusk from high above. He was disappointed. There wasn't one of those lovely notes in Redwing's song, or if there was he failed to hear it. So at last he ventured to ask what may be called a leading question.

"Redwing," said he, "was it you singing way up in the sky after dark the other evening?"

Redwing broke a song off right in the middle and looked down at Peter. "What was that?" he asked as if he hadn't understood, or thought he hadn't.

"I want to know if you sing in the night," said Peter.

"If I do it is in my sleep and I don't know it," retorted Redwing. "Why should I sing in the night?"

"I don't know," confessed Peter. "Somebody does, but no one seems to know who it is."

"Well, it isn't me. You may be sure of that. At night I do what all sensible people do — sleep. When Mr. Sun goes to bed behind the Purple Hills I go to bed too. It is my bedtime," declared Redwing. Then he flew to the topmost twig of an alder and resumed singing.

Now in his curiosity about the mysterious singer in the evening sky Peter had forgotten his recent meeting with Longbill the Woodcock and that the latter had said that Mrs. Longbill was very busy these days sitting still. He was reminded of this when late that very afternoon he came across some of the round holes in the soft ground that he was sure had been made by the long bill of a Woodcock probing for Worms. And then he saw Mrs. Longbill herself.

Had she been squatting perfectly still it is unlikely that Peter would have seen her. It was she who was making those holes. She pulled her long bill out of the ground, swallowed something, then bowed to Peter.

"Hello, Mrs. Longbill! I'm glad to see you back. I certainly am! Longbill told me you were here. He said you were busy sitting still," cried Peter.

"Longbill talks too much," said Mrs. Longbill.

"It is funny I haven't seen you before," said Peter.

"Isn't it? I have been here ever since Longbill got here. If you haven't seen me I've seen you often enough. How comes it you spend so much time over here? I don't remember ever seeing you around here quite so much before. Are you looking for somebody, Peter Rabbit?" replied Mrs. Longbill.

A sudden thought popped into Peter's head. "If you have been here for so long you must have heard a mysterious song up in the sky in the early evening," said he.

"I don't know anything about a *mysterious* song, not a thing," said Mrs. Longbill. "But I do know that every evening my own dear song comes dropping down out of the sky, and that is all the song I care about."

"What?" cried Peter. "Your song? Don't tell me you sing!"

IV. The Mystery Is Solved

Fixed unbelief, try as you will,
You'll find is always hard to kill.

— PETER RABBIT

ON PETER RABBIT'S FACE was a look of complete unbelief. "Don't tell me that you sing," he repeated as he stared at Mrs. Longbill the Woodcock.

"I didn't say so, did I? I didn't say anything of the kind. I said that every night my song comes tumbling down out of the sky," retorted Mrs. Longbill.

"Well, if it is your song you must sing it," snapped Peter testily.

"Who says so? That isn't so at all," declared Mrs. Longbill, beginning to be indignant. "If a song is sung just to me, for the ears of no one but me, it is mine, isn't it? Of course it is. It is just as much my song as if I had sung it myself." She was very positive.

Peter was a little doubtful about this. "You might just as truly say that when I thump a signal to Mrs. Peter it is her signal," said he.

"Certainly. Why not? If it is meant just for her and she gets it, isn't it hers? Of course it is," retorted Mrs. Longbill.

Peter had to think this over. He scratched a long ear with a long hind foot. He shifted and scratched the other long ear with the other long hind foot. He was sure that such a signal would be his own signal, but when Mrs. Longbill put it that way it seemed that there was something in what she said. He didn't see how there could be, yet it sounded reasonable. Finally he gave up puzzling over that. "Who would sing just for you?" he asked bluntly.

"Why Peter, what a question! Who do you think would be likely to sing to me?" replied Mrs. Longbill.

"No one," retorted Peter, then hastened to add, "What I mean is that I can't think of any singer who would be likely to sing just to you."

"Well, of all things!" exclaimed Mrs. Longbill. "I wonder what Longbill would say to that. I just can't imagine him singing to anyone else."

"And I just can't imagine Longbill the Woodcock singing to anyone. I can't imagine him singing at all," declared Peter.

If Mrs. Longbill's black, shoe-button, pop-eyes so nearly on top of her head could have opened any wider they would have. Yes, sir, they would have. "He's a beautiful singer!" she cried.

Peter chuckled. "If you call those whistling sounds that he makes when he flies, or those other funny noises, singing I don't," said he. "They are just sounds, not a song at all. I would as soon expect to sing myself as to hear Longbill really sing. I suppose it is all right for you to think he sings, but other folks are not so fond of him as you are. I guess Longbill himself would laugh if he should hear you call him a singer."

"He *is* a singer," retorted Mrs. Longbill. She was so indignant that she could hardly speak. "I don't call that whistling and those other sounds singing any more than you do. He doesn't either. He sings, and his song is just for me. It is the loveliest song in all the Great World, and you just don't know what you are talking about, Peter Rabbit."

It was clear that Mrs. Longbill meant just what she said. Peter could see that. So he didn't know what to say. He couldn't, he simply *couldn't*, believe that Longbill really sang. Somehow it didn't seem to him possible that a lovely song could come from anyone with such a long bill as a Woodcock's, though why a long bill should have anything to do with it he didn't know. He thought that probably Mrs. Longbill was so much in love with Longbill she would think any sound he might make was lovely. And then Mrs. Longbill said something that set Peter to wondering.

"He sings only at this time of year, and then for only a short time," said she. "When he does sing few ever see him. You see he means that song for me alone. So he waits until it is quite dark. Then he flies high above me where even I cannot see him. There he sings, and his lovely song comes down out of the sky straight from his heart to my heart. When you say he can't sing you don't know what you are talking about. What a pity it is there are so many people like you."

Peter remembered that mysterious song. Could it be, could it possibly be that he had found out who the unknown singer was? He doubted it, yet — well, he would make sure one way or the other. "Where is Longbill?" he demanded.

"Oh, he is around somewhere. Probably he is looking for me in another part of the swamp. I've been teasing him a little by keeping out of his sight. When the dusk is a little deeper he will come to sing to me I am sure," replied Mrs. Longbill.

"I'll stick around," said Peter to himself. "I'll stick around and find out if Longbill really does sing. I still don't believe it."

Mrs. Longbill disappeared, just when or where Peter hadn't the least idea. The truth is that sitting still, doing nothing, Peter had become sleepy. He had been napping without realizing it. Mrs. Longbill had slipped back of a little clump of young alders and squatted down in the dead brown leaves that covered the ground. She looked so like these that Peter might have looked straight at her yet not have seen her.

The dusk had grown quite deep when Peter saw one whom he supposed was Mrs. Longbill quite near him. He was just opening his mouth to ask where she had been when he realized

29

that this wasn't Mrs. Longbill. No, sir, it wasn't Mrs. Longbill. It couldn't be because this person was strutting. Peter had never known Mrs. Longbill to strut. So it must be Longbill himself. It was.

"If people want to be told apart they shouldn't dress alike," thought Peter. "For goodness sake, what is Longbill acting so silly for? I wonder if he knows how silly he looks. I have seen strutting before, but nothing like this."

It was true that Longbill did look funny. Anyway it was funny to eyes for which his strutting was not intended. Perhaps in a barnyard you have seen Gobbler the Turkey strut. Peter had seen Thunderer the Grouse strut, his beautiful tail widespread like a lovely fan, his handsome black ruff also spread wide, his head thrown far back and his wings dropped until the tips touched the ground. He does this for the admiration of Mrs. Grouse. Both Gobbler and Thunderer look important, very important indeed, when they strut.

Longbill strutting didn't look important at all. Not to Peter anyway. He looked funny. To begin with his tail is very short. For a bird he hasn't much more of a tail than has Peter for one of the furry folk. Now he had spread that short tail as wide as he could and cocked it as high as he could. He had thrown back his head as far as he could so that it almost touched his tail. Of course this made his long bill point almost straight up. His wings were dropped almost to the ground. He strutted and bowed in the funniest manner.

30

Peter was just about to ask him what he was doing this for when suddenly he took to his wings. My, how fast they moved! Slanting up through the alders sped Longbill. Well above them he began to circle, rising higher and higher and higher. Peter followed him with his ears, not his eyes. It was too dark for his eyes to follow that skyward flight, but there was no trouble in following it with his ears. Coming down to them was that familiar whistling that he had heard on other evenings. It sounded from higher and higher. It stopped. Then came gently dropping from the sky the lovely notes of the mysterious song that had so puzzled Peter.

"That's it!" he exclaimed. "That's it! Longbill the Woodcock *is* the singer! I never would have believed it had I not been right here to see and hear for myself. No, sir, I never would."

"Didn't I tell you he can sing? And it is for me, just for me. It is *my* song. Isn't it beautiful?" said Mrs. Longbill, appearing suddenly beside Peter.

The song ceased and Mrs. Longbill disappeared. A moment later Longbill was back on the ground at almost the very place from which he had mounted into the sky. Once more he began strutting and bowing. Now, somehow, this didn't look so silly to Peter. But even to this day it is a little difficult for Peter to think of Longbill the Woodcock as one of the sweet singers of the early spring. Yet he is, as Laughing Brook has long known.

"He doesn't look like a singer," protests Peter.

But who shall say how a singer shall look?

V. The Testing of Mrs. Longbill

What-e'er it is you have to do
Have confidence to take you through.

— OLD MOTHER NATURE

WITHOUT CONFIDENCE there can be no success. Mother Nature knows this. So do her children, the furred and feathered folk of the Green Forest and the Green Meadows. Some have confidence in one thing and some in another. Peter Rabbit has confidence in his long heels and the way in which he can dodge. Lightfoot the Deer has confidence in his wonderful nose to warn him of danger. Hooty the Owl has confidence in his marvelous ears and night-seeing eyes. Reddy Fox has confidence in his quick wits. Without confidence, which really is trust or faith, life would be a never-ending fright for most of them.

Longbill the Woodcock and Mrs. Longbill have confidence in their coats. You have confidence in your coat to keep you warm. Just so they have confidence in their coats to keep them from being seen by those they fear. They are ground folk, for Old Mother Nature did not give them feet for perching. So all four-footed hunters, not to mention two-legged hunters with dreadful guns, are enemies to be watched for and to hide from, and they hide in their coats as it were. That is they trust to their coats to keep them from being seen, knowing how closely their coats match in color the fallen leaves on the ground.

Being ground folk of course their nest is on the ground, and they nest early while most of the trees and bushes are still bare. As usual it was Mrs. Longbill who had selected the place for this year's nest. It was in the little swamp through which Laughing Brook enters the Smiling Pool. On a small mound just high enough to be fairly dry grew a clump of young birches. It was at the foot of these that Mrs. Longbill decided the nest should be.

"Don't you think it is a little too open here, my dear?" asked Longbill.

"Not a bit," declared Mrs. Longbill.

"It seems so to me," persisted Longbill.

"Find a better place if you can," snapped Mrs. Longbill. "Ever since we arrived we have been down among the alders. That is where anyone wanting to find us will look. See all the brown leaves covering the ground here, and that little bunch of dead grass. Never have I seen a better place for a nest. There is all the cover we need. No one is going to find the nest unless one of us is careless."

Longbill had to admit to himself that she had some reason for her confidence, so there the nest was placed. As a nest it was nothing to brag about, merely a slight depression lined with a few dead leaves and a little, a very little, dry grass. Empty it didn't look like a nest. Had you happened to see it then you probably wouldn't have suspected it was a nest.

It was the day after the fourth egg was laid that Mrs. Longbill and her confidence were first put to the test, and it was a test! Longbill saw it. He was just a little way off hunting for Worms in the soft ground. He was very busy boring holes after those Worms but not too busy to be watchful. So it was that he saw Reddy Fox enter the swamp and begin to move back and forth through it with his nose set to catch any telltale scent, and his sharp eyes watching for any movement.

"Hunting for us," thought Longbill, squatting close to the ground. "He knows we are back and probably nesting now. He hopes to find our nest and catch one of us on it. I wish it was better hidden."

He saw Reddy turn toward that little mound with the clump of birches and his heart sank. Yes, sir, his heart sank. He didn't much fear that Mrs. Longbill would be caught. He had no doubt that she saw Reddy. She could take to her swift wings, and would if she had to. But if and when she did Reddy would find those precious eggs.

Longbill held his breath. Reddy was so close to Mrs. Longbill that it seemed as if he might step on her. Why, oh why, didn't she fly? She didn't move, not so much as a feather. Reddy left the little mound and continued hunting in another part of the swamp. Finally he left the swamp. He had almost stepped on Mrs. Longbill yet hadn't seen her, nor had he found her scent. Those keen eyes and that wonderful nose had failed him completely, yet there was nothing whatever wrong with them. It was because of three things — Mrs. Longbill's resemblance to her surroundings, her ability to withhold her scent by compressing her feathers, and her magnificent courage, keeping so still that not even a feather moved. U. S. 706839

She had seen Reddy long before he was near enough to be dangerous. She could have slipped from her eggs and flown away as well as not. But doing that would have exposed those precious eggs. So she had remained covering them, lying as flat as possible, her neck stretched out along the ground. Her coat blended so perfectly with the brown leaves around her that without movement she seemed a part of her surroundings. It had taken courage, a very great deal of courage, and supreme confidence, to do what she had done.

"What did I tell you? Didn't I say that this is the safest place for a nest?" she cried triumphantly when Longbill told her that he had seen it all.

But the very next day Mrs. Longbill's nerves, courage and confidence had even a harder test. Farmer Brown's boy had a friend who had a Dog trained to hunt game birds. These are the birds that hunters with terrible guns delight to shoot, why I don't know. No dead bird is truly interesting. A live bird always is. Woodcocks are among these game birds. Grouse, Pheasant and Bob Whites are others. All of them give off scent that the wonderful noses of certain kinds of Dogs can smell and follow. These Dogs have been trained to follow the scent until they find just where a bird is, then stand still and point to the hiding place.

This was not the hunting season, but the friend of Farmer Brown's boy never had seen the nest of a Woodcock and was anxious to. He had seen Longbill in that swamp and suspected that there was a nest. He was sure that if one of the birds was on the nest his Dog would find it. Reluctantly Farmer Brown's boy had agreed to allow the Dog to try, and had come along to watch.

Just as Reddy Fox had done the Dog ran this way and that, all the time using his nose. Once he stopped suddenly. He stood as if frozen. With nose and one lifted forefoot he was pointing to a certain spot. His master went there and up flew Longbill on whistling wings. Then began a careful search all around that spot for the nest, but no nest was found. Farmer Brown's boy grinned.

A little later all three, the Dog, his master, and Farmer Brown's boy, stood on a little mound beside a clump of young birches. Almost at their feet Mrs. Longbill covered her precious eggs, her head flattened among the leaves. The Dog all but stepped on her as he sniffed in vain.

"There is no nest around here or my Dog would have found it," said his master. "I'm disappointed," he continued. "I was sure that we would find a Woodcock on her nest somewhere in this swamp. There isn't one or Sport would have found it." Sport was the Dog's name.

Farmer Brown's boy hid a smile as he said, "You have a lot of faith in Sport, haven't you?"

"There isn't a better bird Dog in the state," boasted Sport's master. "If there is a Woodcock anywhere about Sport will find it, just as he found that one a little while ago. Do you know what I think?"

"What do you think?" asked Farmer Brown's boy.

"I think it is a little too early in the season for Woodcock to be nesting," was the reply. "If we didn't have Sport along I would think that we might have overlooked a nest. Of course he couldn't find it unless one of the birds was on it, so there is just a chance that there is a nest somewhere around here and the birds have not begun sitting. So we might try again next week. You can count on Sport to find a Woodcock if there is one around. He has a great nose, has that Dog."

"Supposing a bird on the nest didn't want to be smelled?" suggested Farmer Brown's boy.

The other laughed. "Well, supposing it didn't; what could he or she do about it?" said he.

"I wonder," replied Farmer Brown's boy. "I have read that a bird on the nest can withhold scent so that a Dog cannot smell it even when close by."

"Pooh! I don't believe that!" exclaimed the other. "I would like to see the Woodcock that could keep Sport from smelling her if he were within smelling distance. I guess that is just a story. Don't you?"

Farmer Brown's boy turned his head quickly to hide his sudden grin. "Maybe it is true and that is why Sport failed to find Mrs. Longbill on her nest," said he. He glanced down at what looked like a pair of black shoe buttons lying on the leaves almost at their feet. He had seen them when he first arrived there and recognized them for a pair of eyes. Knowing what to look for he had at once traced the outline of Mrs. Longbill, so motionless that it was difficult for even his trained eyes to separate her from the surrounding leaves.

They moved on, Sport running ahead. Farmer Brown's boy looked back over his shoulder to see if Mrs. Longbill would move after they had left. She didn't. He chuckled, a little inside silent chuckle. "Your secret is safe with me, Mrs. Longbill," said he to himself. "You were almost stepped on yet didn't give yourself away, and I won't give you away."

VI. Handsome but Modest

No matter what it is you do
You work for self and others too.
— SLAPTAIL THE BEAVER

JERRY MUSKRAT had been exploring up Laughing Brook a little way into the Green Forest. Now he was back in the Smiling Pool.

"My dear," said he to Mrs. Jerry, "do stop worrying about a flood. There isn't going to be one this year. Not here anyway."

"How do you know that?" Mrs. Jerry asked sharply.

"I met Billy Mink. He said he had been way up Laughing Brook to an old pond of Paddy the Beaver. Paddy's son, Slaptail, and family are living there now. He told Billy Mink that he and his folks farther up have the water under control," explained Jerry.

"I don't believe it," declared Mrs. Jerry flatly. "No one can control Laughing Brook. There always has been a flood in the spring and there always will be."

"Not any more. We have had high water this year, but not a flood, and there won't be one. We have had our house washed away for the last time as long as the Beaver folk continue to live along Laughing Brook. They have ponds enough now to keep it in control," declared Jerry.

"Who says so?" demanded Mrs. Jerry.

"Slaptail," replied Jerry. "He ought to know. He told Billy his folks have dams and ponds at different places all the way to where Laughing Brook starts way up on the Great Mountain, and these hold back the water so that too much cannot rush down all at once."

"I hope he knows what he is talking about," squeaked Mrs. Jerry. Her voice always is squeaky.

"He does," said Beauty the Wood Duck. With Mrs. Beauty he had just arrived from the Sunny South.

"What do you know about it?" demanded Mrs. Jerry crossly.

"I know a lot about it. Last fall before leaving I looked over all their ponds," replied Beauty.

"Oh," said Mrs. Jerry lamely.

"So you really think we have the Beaver folk to thank for having no flood to worry about?" questioned Jerry.

"I know it," declared the handsome little Duck. "Sometimes I wonder if there are any more useful and important folks than the

Beavers in all the Great World. I don't know any others who do as much good for other folks as they do. Mrs. Beauty and I are everlastingly obliged to them."

"You're what?" cried Jerry.

"Obliged to them; everlastingly obliged to them," replied Beauty.

"For what?" Jerry asked bluntly.

"For providing us with such perfect places each year to make our home and bring up a family. But for them we might often have had to travel far and look long," explained Beauty.

"How have they done that? What have Beavers to do with Ducks?" Jerry wanted to know. He looked doubtful.

Beauty shook his handsome head. "I'm sorry for folks who never travel," said he. "I truly am. Now if you had traveled as Mrs. Beauty and I have, and had visited farther north where there are many Beaver folk, you never would have asked what Beavers have to do with Ducks. We Wood Ducks like to nest in hollow trees and we are most likely to find those in the Green Forest. But we want to be near water. After all we are water birds. So we must find ponds in the Green Forest. The Beaver folk make the ponds for us."

"They make them for themselves," retorted Jerry.

"True, but in so doing they make them for us too. What is more, they are glad to have us for neighbors. They work hard for themselves, but they share the results with others and are glad to. That is the way it should be with everybody. As I said before I don't know any other folks who are as useful to their neighbors, or do as much good for others," declared Beauty, and he meant it.

Now all this time, partly hidden by some bunch grass, Peter Rabbit had been sitting quietly at the edge of the water listening. He had just opened his mouth to ask some questions when there were new arrivals in the Smiling Pool. They were Mr. and Mrs. Quack the Mallard Ducks. They had come up from the Big River. Mr. Quack with his bright green head and neck, his white collar and his rich chestnut breast, was handsome. There was no question about that. Even so he seemed almost plain beside little Beauty.

To begin with Beauty wore a wonderful crest that hung down at the back. His head, including the crest, was green and blue and purple. On each side, beginning at the base of the bill, there was a line of white over the eye. There was a similar line below. His throat was white and there was a band of white up each side of his head. He also wore a handsome chestnut waistcoat. In front of the wings was a white band. On his back he was brown and purple and green, and his wings were velvety black with white and purple and blue. His eyes were red and his feet and legs orange. He was lovely. Peter felt that he would never tire of looking at him.

Mrs. Beauty wore a smaller crest and was much more plainly dressed. But she was a dainty and trim person, very trim indeed.

"Are you going on farther north or will you stay around here?" asked Peter when Beauty swam near.

"Hello, Peter!" exclaimed Beauty as if seeing him for the

first time. "We haven't decided yet. We haven't been here long enough for that. Perhaps we will look around a bit anyway."

"You better stay. You won't find any better place farther north," declared Peter.

Mr. and Mrs. Quack, who were listening, chuckled. So did the Wood Ducks. "My, how wise you are!" exclaimed Mr. Quack. "Since when have you known all about farther north, Peter Rabbit?"

Peter looked a little confused. "Well, anyway it is nice around here," said he.

"It is pleasant," agreed Beauty. "When Mrs. Beauty and I have rested a bit we will look around. You know, unlike most other Ducks, we do not make our nest on the ground so it takes some looking around to find the right place. We build in a tree."

"You won't have any trouble in finding a tree around here. The Green Forest is full of trees," said Peter and wondered why the four Ducks were chuckling.

Presently Beauty and Mrs. Beauty took to their wings, disappearing over the treetops. Peter was disappointed. He thought they had left to go farther on.

"I don't see why they should have been in such a hurry. It was only this morning that they got here," said he.

"Probably they are anxious to begin nesting," said Mrs. Quack, a twinkle in her eyes. And with this Peter had to be content.

Later he wandered a little way back in the swamp. He was still wondering why those Ducks had been in such a hurry to leave. There came the whistling of swift wings overhead.

Through the tree tops he had a glimpse of two Ducks headed toward the Smiling Pool.

"I do believe Beauty and Mrs. Beauty have come back," thought Peter, and scampered for the Smiling Pool. When he got there, sure enough, there were Mr. and Mrs. Beauty. "So you decided to come back, did you?" cried Peter.

"No. We simply decided to stay," replied Beauty.

"But you flew away," cried Peter. "Why did you change your minds and return?"

"We didn't change our minds. You see we hadn't made them up. We went up Laughing Brook to look things over and see if we could find a tree," replied Beauty.

"The Green Forest is full of trees," said Peter.

Beauty chuckled. "So it is, Peter. So it is. But we found only one that would do for us," said he.

Peter thought of all the big trees in the Green Forest. "You must be fussy," said he.

It was Mrs. Beauty who spoke now. "We are," said she. "We are very fussy. A tree must be just right or it will not do at all. Sometimes we have to go quite a distance from water to find one. That is bad. This time we found one that is just right. It couldn't be better. So we are going to stay."

"Where is it?" asked Peter bluntly.

"That is for you to find out if you really want to know," replied Beauty, and the four Ducks, for Mr. and Mrs. Quack had been listening, chuckled as if they were enjoying a joke. Peter wondered what it was.

VII. Mrs. Quack's Change of Mind

He best will live who will arrange
His way of life to constant change.

— OLD MOTHER NATURE

OLD MOTHER NATURE KNOWS. One of her basic laws is the law of change, and success in living depends on acceptance of it. Those who cannot or will not change with changing surroundings and conditions are certain to fail in the art of successful living. Thus changing one's mind often becomes not only a privilege but a duty to self and others. So it is that a change of mind may be a sign of progress.

Mr. and Mrs. Quack, the Mallard Ducks, on the way from their winter stay in the Sunny South to their usual nesting ground in the Far North, had stopped at the Smiling Pool as they had often done in other years. It was one of their regular resting places on the long spring flight. They had looked forward to getting there. Perhaps they remembered the corn that Farmer Brown's boy had scattered there in other seasons especially for them. He had this time.

It was good to be back. They found Jerry Muskrat and Mrs. Jerry at home and feeling very cheerful because there had been no spring flood and there was not likely to be one because the Beaver folk had Laughing Brook under control by means of their ponds scattered along it.

They had found Beauty the Wood Duck and Mrs. Beauty already there. They were old friends and the four Ducks had much to talk about. Then Beauty and Mrs. Beauty had flown up Laughing Brook. Later they returned and announced that they had decided to stay instead of going on farther as they had expected to. They had found at one of the old ponds of Paddy the Beaver a place that just suited them, so what was the use of going farther? There wasn't any use, so they were going to stay.

"We'll never find anything to suit us better," declared Mrs. Beauty. "You folks really should have a look at those ponds before going on. You really should."

"Perhaps we will," replied Mrs. Quack, and Mr. Quack nodded his handsome green head.

"If you do you may change your minds about going on," said Beauty.

The very next day the Quacks started up Laughing Brook. After a time they came to a pond. It wasn't a big pond. In it was a house and near this Slaptail, son of Paddy the Beaver, was swimming. He was joined by Mrs. Slaptail. This was their home pond. The two Ducks paid their respects to the Slaptails and then looked the pond and its surroundings all over.

"If you are looking for a place to make your home we'll be glad to have you stay here," said Slaptail.

They thanked him and said they might be back. Then they went on up Laughing Brook. Soon they came to the place where the first of Paddy the Beaver's ponds had once been. That was a long time ago. Having used up all the food trees around it Paddy and Mrs. Paddy had moved on to where food could be obtained and there had built new dams, making new ponds. With no one to keep the old dam in repair it had gradually gone to pieces and most of the water had drained away, leaving only a big pool where the pond had been deepest beside Paddy's big house. This was now more or less in ruins, grass and weeds growing on the roof. What had been a fairly big pond was now a rich wild meadow with grass of several kinds, flowers and other plants, covering what had been the bottom of the pond. Through it ran Laughing Brook. Around that meadow grew the trees of the Green Forest.

Mrs. Quack sat on the roof of Paddy's old house while Mr.

Quack idled in the pool below. It was quiet and pleasant there.

"I've changed my mind," said Mrs. Quack at last.

Mr. Quack didn't look surprised. "What about?" he asked.

"About going on to our old nesting place in the Far North," replied Mrs. Quack. "We are going to stay here."

"Are we?" asked Mr. Quack mildly.

"Yes," replied Mrs. Quack. "I don't know just where we will make our nest, but we will find a place. We'll look around until we do. I am sure we will find just what we want somewhere in the neighborhood."

With Mrs. Quack in the lead they looked that meadow all over. Not far above it they found two more small ponds that the Beavers had made but were no longer using. Mrs. Quack examined every foot of the shores of these. There were several places that she spent much time in looking over. None just suited her. There was always the feeling that they would find a better place.

Back at Paddy's old house beside the pool in the meadow they rested. There was something about that old house that gave Mrs. Quack a sort of home feeling. An old house has a home feeling a new house can never have. The longer it has been lived in the more of that home feeling is in and around it. It is called an atmosphere, and the older a house is the more of this it has, for in it are the joys, sorrows, hopes, fears, loves, hates, dreams, ambitions, sufferings, rejoicings — all the things that entered into the lives of those who once lived there. An old house may have long been empty but the atmosphere remains. Perhaps it was this that Mrs. Quack felt there at Paddy the Beaver's old house.

"I am glad Cousin Beauty suggested that we come up here before going on," said Mrs. Quack. "It is a perfect neighborhood in which to make our home and raise a family. There is plenty of food and plenty of water. Our Wood Duck cousins will have a nest in a tree somewhere around here, and you and Beauty will be company for each other while Mrs. Beauty and I are sitting on our precious eggs. I wish I could make up my mind just where to make our nest. Have you any ideas?"

Mr. Quack shook his handsome green head and admitted that there wasn't an idea in it. He knew from experience that it would be Mrs. Quack's ideas, not his, that would decide where that nest would be. "I leave that wholly to you, my dear," said he. "You know best where a nest should be. You are the one who will use it, not me. Suit yourself and I will be suited.

So Mrs. Quack continued to look and Mr. Quack continued to tag along. After a while he did wish that she would make up her mind. He was getting tired of following her around that meadow and those two ponds, to say nothing of trips up and down Laughing Brook. Mrs. Quack was nothing if not thorough. She examined every bit of shore and then did it over again. Sometimes they waddled some distance back from the water to some likely place that looked as if a nest might be well hidden there. Sometimes Mr. Quack waited on the water, not too patiently I suspect, while she went ashore.

Sooner or later they would be back at Paddy's old house by the pool in the meadow. Each time Mrs. Quack did the same thing. She climbed out on it and waddled all over it. She sat down here, snuggled down there, and squatted down elsewhere.

"You seem to like this old house," said Mr. Quack.

"I do," replied Mrs. Quack. "There is something about it that gives me a sort of at home feeling that I haven't found anywhere else. I don't know why, but that is the way I feel as soon as I come in sight of it. I feel as if I am coming home; as if I belong here."

Of course it was the atmosphere of the old house. She felt it without knowing what it was. Perhaps there are no such big words in the Duck language.

"I guess you have looked at every blade of grass on that roof," remarked Mr. Quack as Mrs. Quack returned to her favorite resting spot. For a long time she sat there dreamily watching Mr. Quack swimming about before her, displaying all his fine feathers, showing off; trying to convince her that he was the handsomest fellow in all the Great World. Suddenly, with no warning at all, Mrs. Quack jumped to her feet, lifted her head high and quacked excitedly.

"Quack, quack, quack, quack! I know exactly where our nest is to be!" quacked she.

"Where?" asked Mr. Quack.

"Right here. Right where I am sitting this very minute. I am going to make it right on this very spot," cried Mrs. Quack.

She did.

VIII. The Sawbills Arrive

In isolation you will find
The concepts of a narrow mind.
— OLD MOTHER NATURE

FOLKS WHO ARE neither busy nor strong of mind need the company of others. They lack self-sufficiency. They are dependent on others to get them away from themselves. They must talk to others and be talked to even though what is said is of no consequence.

On the grass-and-weed-grown roof of Paddy the Beaver's old house Mrs. Quack had made her nest. Sitting on her precious eggs she peeped out over the tree-girt Beaver meadow and dreamed happily of the ducklings that would one day follow her into the little pool below for their first swim. She was a picture of dreamy contentment.

It wasn't so with Mr. Quack. He had nothing to do but grow tired of himself, and grow more and more lonesome despite the nearness of Mrs. Quack. He couldn't sit by the nest and talk to her lest he be seen and their precious secret discovered. He missed the gatherings of the drakes, as father Ducks are called, which were daily affairs in their old northern home where there were many nests in the neighborhood. So now he spent much time visiting with Beauty the Wood Duck in one of the little ponds a little way up Laughing Brook. They had become quite chummy, those two. In a hole high up in a dead tree standing in the water Mrs. Beauty, like Mrs. Quack, was sitting on eggs. She left them only long enough to get food.

This morning as Mr. Quack and Beauty idled near the upper end of the pond a pair of fast flying folks suddenly appeared coming up Laughing Brook. They were flying low over the water. They circled the pond, then went on up Laughing Brook toward the second pond.

"The Sawbills!" exclaimed Beauty. "I wonder if we are to have them for neighbors. I am glad we got here first."

"Why?" asked Mr. Quack. "What difference would it have made had they arrived first?"

Beauty nodded his handsome head toward the lone tree in the water. "They might have taken that tree for their home. Mrs. Beauty declares that it is the best home we have had for a long time," said he.

Mr. Quack looked up at the hole high in the lone tree. It had been cut long before by Logcock the Pileated Woodpecker, largest but one, Ivory Bill, of the Woodpecker family. He shook his handsome green head. He couldn't understand any Duck nesting in such a place as that. "Are you telling me that the Sawbills also nest in holes in trees?" he demanded.

"Not always, but sometimes. When they do they show good sense if you ask me," replied the Wood Duck. "With holes in trees getting more scarce every year it is hard to find a good empty house if we happen to be a little late in getting back in the spring. That house up there is the only one of the kind anywhere in the neighborhood. I know because Mrs. Beauty and I looked everywhere. Had those Sawbills arrived first and decided to stay they would have moved right in and we would have had to go on farther."

"I am glad they didn't," said Mr. Quack.

"So am I," replied Beauty.

"If holes in trees are so hard to find I am glad we Mallards don't use them. We always can find a good nesting place on the ground," said Mr. Quack.

Beauty shook his head. "Not for us," said he. "We Wood Ducks don't like nesting on the ground. Of course we might do it if we could find no better place, but if we did we wouldn't feel easy for a minute. No, sir, we wouldn't. When she is sitting on eggs Mrs. Beauty wants a roof over her head and stout dry walls around her. Hello! Here they come back!"

Sure enough the Sawbills were returning. They splashed

onto the water at the lower end of the pond. Then one began swimming towards them.

"It looks as if we are to have company," said Mr. Quack in a low voice.

Sawbill rapidly drew near. He swam with his head held high on his long slim neck. He had a crest which was slightly raised. His head was greenish-black. His bill, instead of being broad, more or less flat and rounded as most Duck bills are, was long, narrow and at the tip slightly hooked. The edges were toothed like a saw. Now you know why he is called Sawbill. He is also called Shelldrake and Fish Duck, but his real name is American Merganser. He was an old acquaintance of the others.

"Are you fellows staying around here for the summer?" he asked as he joined them.

The others nodded. "Are you?" asked Mr. Quack.

"I don't know yet. Mrs. Sawbill hasn't said. I leave such matters to her," replied Sawbill.

"We understand," said the others together, nodding their handsome heads.

"I thought you would," replied Sawbill. "There is nothing like letting the ladies suit themselves, think they are having their own way. Then there is no one they can blame when things are not as they expected. This neighborhood looks good to me. It does so. But whether or not we will stay depends on finding a place to nest, and on what Mrs. Sawbill thinks of it. Here she comes now."

Sawbill swam to meet Mrs. Sawbill. He was most attentive to her. He knew how to show off his fine appearance to the best advantage and he did. He paid her every attention, as if she were the most important person in all the Great World. She was to him, just then anyway. He escorted her over to the others. She scarcely glanced at them. Her keen eyes had seen the hole high up in the lone tree in the water. She headed straight for that tree and lifted her wings a little, preparing to fly up to that hole.

"That house is occupied. You're too late," said Beauty hastily.

Just then Mrs. Beauty put her head out of the doorway to see what was going on. Mrs. Sawbill gave her tail an angry flirt and turned her back to the tree. Have you noticed how very often disappointment makes folks angry? Plainly Mrs. Sawbill was disappointed. She gave her head a quick toss. "Come on," she commanded sharply.

Meekly Sawbill followed her around the pond close to the shore, then up Laughing Brook to the other pond, which was very near. For the next few days they were seen only occasionally. Sometimes they came flying up Laughing Brook. Sometimes they came flying down Laughing Brook. When Sawbill was asked where they had been and what they had been doing he replied vaguely. "Oh, just looking around," he would say.

"If you are looking for a hollow tree like ours that is empty you won't find one in this part of the Green Forest." Beauty spoke positively. He was positive.

"We are not particular about a hollow tree," replied Sawbill. "There are other places for nests that we like just as well. We have seen several fairly good ones. But Mrs. Sawbill hasn't yet fully made up her mind that she wants to stay around here instead of going on."

"Who says she hasn't?" demanded Mrs. Sawbill harshly. Unnoticed she had drawn near enough to overhear.

"But my dear," began Sawbill.

Mrs. Sawbill cut him short. "Never mind that," said she. "You come with me. I have something to show you."

She led the way to the other little pond. Near the shore of this, back just a little and partly hidden by young spruce trees growing on all sides of it, was the fairly high stump of a big tree that had been broken off in a great wind long ago. The top of this stump was hollowed out somewhat, as the tops of such old stumps so often are. Mrs. Sawbill flew up on the edge of it. Sawbill flew up beside her. He looked at the hollow, then looked at Mrs. Sawbill. In his eyes was an unspoken question.

"This is it," said she softly. He knew by her tone that there was no question but she had found what she had been looking for.

"You mean you are going to make a nest here?" asked Sawbill, although he knew the answer.

"What else could I mean?" said Mrs. Sawbill a bit testily. "There couldn't be a more perfect place for a nest. It is so well hidden by these green trees that I passed it several times without seeing it. We'll begin building at once."

"You mean you will," thought Sawbill, but he didn't say it. At the first opportunity he joined Mr. Quack and Beauty to tell them that it was all settled that he and Mrs. Sawbill were to stay.

IX. A Growing Neighborhood

Heed not the gossip if you would
Be friendly in your neighborhood.
— OLD MOTHER NATURE

EACH HAS HIS OWN appointed place in his neighborhood. Alas, that so many people seem not to know this. It is the cause of most neighborhood troubles. A place for everybody and everybody in his place would make a new and infinitely better world.

Longlegs the Great Blue Heron had flown from the Big River up Laughing Brook to the Smiling Pool. There he stopped to fish. Later he flew on up Laughing Brook through the Green Forest until he came to two small old ponds of Paddy the Beaver very near together. At one of these he checked his flight, dropped

59

his long legs to stand at the edge of the water, raised his great wings high above his back, folded them back in place, stretched his long neck to full height, and with his keen eyes looked over the pond and surroundings.

On a dead tree near the water sat King Eagle, he of the snowy head and tail. On the water at the far side were three old acquaintances. With heads held high they sat still watching him. They were Mr. Quack, Beauty and Sawbill, the Mallard, Wood Duck and Merganser cousins. On the shore beyond them, running along at the edge of the water, were the Spotted Sandpipers, Mr. and Mrs. Teeter. Whenever they stopped they teetered and bobbed and bowed as if trying to keep their uncertain balance on their slender little legs.

Sure that no enemy was about Longlegs folded his long neck back on his shoulders, tipping his head so that he could watch the water and ground just ahead of him. With slow, stately steps he walked along the shore at the very edge of the water. A small fish darted out for deeper water. He wasn't quick enough. The head of Longlegs, with its great spearlike bill, shot out and down. Then that little fish was on its way down inside the long neck instead of out into deeper water.

Presently the big Heron spread his great wings. With his long legs straight out behind him he flew to the wild meadow where once had been Paddy the Beaver's first pond. He lighted at the edge of the big pool beside Paddy's old house. From a nest hidden in the grass and weeds growing on the roof of that old house a pair of bright eyes watched him. He didn't see them. He had eyes only for a small Frog sitting on the base of the old house at the edge of the water. Again that head with the great bill shot forward and down. This time it was Longlegs who was not quick enough. Plop! That little Frog had dived into the water and disappeared in the mud of the bottom.

In the bright eyes watching from the nest on the roof was a pleased look. They were the eyes of Mrs. Quack. She and Longlegs were old acquaintances, but for all that she wasn't sorry that he had been too slow. Every day since she had begun sitting on her eggs that little Frog had sat there just below. He was company for her even though he probably didn't even know she was there.

Longlegs began to stalk about over the meadow where the ground was wet and marshy. He was looking the place over while at the same time watching for something more for breakfast. Once he caught a Frog and twice he missed. Failure didn't appear to trouble him at all, perhaps because long ago he had learned that often it is failure that leads to success. After a while he took to his great wings and flew off down Laughing Brook the way he had come.

"Fish in the ponds and Frogs in the meadow. I must bring Mrs. Longlegs up here. This looks to me like just the place for us to spend the summer," thought he as with measured beats of his great wings he disappeared toward the Big River.

"Good riddance," Sawbill had said as the three Ducks in the little pond watched the big Heron when he left there.

"Why?" asked Mr. Quack.

"Didn't you see him catch the little fish when he first got here?" asked Sawbill.

"Certainly, but what of it?" replied Mr. Quack.

"Any fish that are to be caught Mrs. Sawbill and I want. That is why we have decided to stay here," Sawbill replied.

"Well, he has gone. Perhaps he won't come back," said Mr. Quack.

"He will," declared Sawbill darkly.

He was right. Late that very afternoon Longlegs returned and with him was Mrs. Longlegs. She had come somewhat unwillingly as she had about made up her mind that they would return to their old nesting place farther up the Big River. But she had only to fly once around the two small ponds and the Beaver meadow to drop all idea of going farther.

"It is a wonderful neighborhood. It really is," she croaked to Longlegs. Her voice always sounds like a croak. "We'll find plenty of Frogs in this meadow and plenty of fish in the ponds and brook. It is wonderfully quiet and secluded all around here. I couldn't ask a better neighborhood in which to bring up a family. I have already picked out the tree in which to build our nest."

The very next day Sawbill saw Mrs. Longlegs walking about among the trees a little back from the water. She picked up a stick. She dropped it and picked up another. This she also dropped for a third. With this in her bill she flew away.

"You know what that means," Sawbill said darkly to Mrs. Sawbill after telling her what he had seen.

62

"What does it mean?" she asked, just as if she had no idea.

"It means she has begun to build a nest. It means that she and Longlegs have decided to stay in this neighborhood," replied Sawbill. He didn't look at all happy about it.

"What do you care?" asked Mr. Quack the Mallard Duck, who happened to be near.

"They'll spoil the fishing for us," said Sawbill.

"Perhaps they think you'll spoil the fishing for them," retorted Mr. Quack.

"We got here first," said Sawbill. "Have you ever seen one of their nests?" he added.

"No," replied Mr. Quack. "We never have happened to be neighbors of theirs in the nesting season. Do they build a good nest?"

"Sticks," replied Sawbill scornfully.

"Nothing but sticks?" asked Mr. Quack.

"Nothing but sticks, and sometimes when a nest is new not too many of those," replied Sawbill.

Mr. Quack thought of the bed of soft down Mrs. Quack had pulled from her own breast to line their nest. "I guess," said he, "that the babies don't stay in a nest like that any longer than they must. Is the nest on the ground or in a tree?"

"In a tree and high up too as a rule. Look! There's Mrs. Longlegs with another stick! That settles it." Sawbill sounded disgusted.

"Settles what?" asked Mr. Quack.

"Those long-legged fish eaters are going to stay. Yes, sir, they are going to stay. There isn't any doubt about it," declared Sawbill.

"What of it? I'm willing," said Mr. Quack.

"You don't live on fish," retorted Sawbill.

"I guess there are fish enough for them and you too," said Mr. Quack, watching Mrs. Longlegs fly off with a stick.

"Besides," continued Sawbill as if he hadn't heard, "they are likely to bring friends back here with them next spring. They are queer folks if you ask me. Excepting when nesting they keep by themselves, but when it comes time for nesting they often seem to like a lot of neighbors of their own kind. That is just the time I should think they would want to be by themselves. But that seems to be the way of the Heron family. Speaking of Herons, look over on the end of that old log in the water on the other side of the pond."

Mr. Quack looked. "Why, it is little Poke!" he exclaimed. He meant the Little Green Heron, smallest of the family.

"And as I live there is Quawk the Night Heron!" Sawbill looked as disgusted as he sounded.

"I'm glad I'm not a fish or a Frog," chuckled Mr. Quack.

"This neighborhood is growing too fast," grumbled Sawbill.

X. Who Was It?

A careless look, a wandering glance,
And lo, a secret found by chance!
— BEAUTY THE WOOD DUCK

PETER RABBIT was full of curiosity. This was nothing new. He always is full of curiosity. However, this time it seemed as if he was more curious than ever, and it was all because of Mr. and Mrs. Beauty the Wood Ducks. He had met them at the Smiling Pool when they had arrived from the Sunny South. He had watched them fly up Laughing Brook into the Green Forest. He had seen them return and Beauty had said that they had found a tree to suit them and had decided to stay instead of going farther north as they had expected to.

It was the matter of the tree that puzzled Peter and filled him with curiosity concerning Mr. and Mrs. Beauty. He knew that

66

Mrs. Quack the Mallard Duck made her nest on the ground, and that Mrs. Black Duck did also. Somehow it was difficult to think of Ducks making nests in trees. Somehow it didn't make sense. Not to Peter anyway. He wanted to see a Duck's nest in a tree. He felt that until he did he couldn't really believe there could be such a thing. So when Beauty said that they had found a tree to suit them Peter asked right away where it was.

"That is for you to find out," Beauty had replied and he and Mrs. Beauty had chuckled.

Of course Peter had had no business to ask such a question. Certainly not. He knew it. The homes of the Green Meadows and Green Forest folks are their own precious secrets as long as they can keep them secret. This is for safety. So Peter hadn't really expected to be told where that tree was.

"Those Wood Ducks are small for Ducks. Still they are big enough to need a fairly big nest, one big enough to be easily seen up in a tree," thought Peter. "That tree is somewhere up Laughing Brook and of course it is near the water. After the nest is built I should have no trouble in finding it," thought Peter.

So he waited a week or more before venturing up Laughing Brook to look for that nest. He was staying over in the Green Forest these days. He was getting a long way from home, much farther than he should be. Still he kept on. Curiosity wouldn't allow him to turn back. Curiosity often is like that. Besides, there was so much to see. As he went along he kept looking up in the trees along Laughing Brook but saw nothing that looked like a nest.

At long last he reached the small pond where Beauty and Mrs. Beauty were living. At first he didn't show himself. At least he didn't know that he did. He thought that by watching those Ducks he might find out where their nest was.

"Anyway I should be able to find out in what direction that tree is. Then I will know which way to look," thought he.

Now Beauty had seen Peter soon after he reached the pond and he had guessed what had brought Peter up there and why he was taking such pains to keep from being seen.

"We'll tease him a little," said Beauty to Mrs. Beauty. "We'll leave the pond and return in different directions." And that is just what they did.

Peter would see Beauty coming from a certain direction. He would swim about a while then leave in another direction. The same thing would happen with Mrs. Beauty. It seemed to Peter that they never came twice from the same direction nor left twice in the same direction. It was most confusing and upsetting. After a day or two of this Peter decided that he was just wasting time.

"The thing to do is to look in all the big trees near this pond," thought Peter. "They wouldn't have built very far back from the pond. After all they are water birds. Probably they make their nest of sticks. Anyway whatever it is made of it must be big and easy to see."

So Peter wandered about looking up in big trees until his neck ached. He even left the pond and wandered farther up

68

Laughing Brook. Twice he thought he had found the nest only to discover that he was mistaken. One was a Crow's nest, an old one not in use. The other was a Squirrel's old nest now falling to pieces.

Peter began to doubt if those Ducks had a nest. Sometimes he saw them together on the water, but more often Beauty was alone. This happened more and more frequently until finally it was rarely that he had a glimpse of Mrs. Beauty.

Then one day Beauty swam in close to where Peter was sitting. "Where is Mrs. Beauty?" asked Peter.

Beauty's eyes twinkled. "Attending to her duty," he replied.
"And what is that?" asked Peter.

"Sitting on our eggs," replied the beautiful little Duck.

Peter sighed. "Then you really and truly have a nest," said he.
"In a tree?"

"In a tree," replied Beauty.

"Then it must be a long way from here for I have looked
in all the big trees anywhere near here," said Peter.

Beauty chuckled softly. He was still chuckling as he swam
away. Peter wondered what he was chuckling about.

Early the next morning Peter was sitting under a small hemlock tree a little back from the water. He had decided to give
up looking for that nest, so now he had nothing special on his
mind. His stomach was full and he was just daydreaming. In the
water a little way from him stood a dead tree, so long dead that
even the bark had peeled from it. Halfway up it was a hole.
It was quite a large hole. Peter guessed that the big Woodpecker
called Logcock and his mate had made it a long time ago.

"I wonder if anybody has lived in it since those big Wood-
peckers gave it up," thought Peter.

Suddenly he sat up straight, his long ears standing straight
up like exclamation points, his eyes wide with surprise. "I saw
something move in that hole!" he exclaimed under his breath.
"I know I did. It must be that someone is living there right
now. Probably it is one of the Owl family. I'll sit right here
until I find out."

70

So Peter made himself comfortable and kept his eyes on that hole in the dead tree. Two or three times he thought he saw something or someone moving just inside that doorway, but he wasn't sure because of the darkness inside. He continued to be patient, and he can be very, very patient when he wants to be. At long last his patience was rewarded. A head was suddenly thrust out of that hole and as quickly withdrawn.

Peter gave a little gasp. Yes, sir, he did so. Then he rubbed his eyes. "Did I or didn't I?" he muttered. "I did, yet I couldn't have. I must have dreamed it. Such a thing couldn't be. I certainly am seeing things."

It was true, for it happened again. A head was poked out of that hole in the tree and withdrawn as quickly, and that head was the head of a Duck. Peter was sure of it. But whoever heard of Ducks in holes in trees, holes high up from the ground? Peter hadn't and this was why he couldn't make himself believe his own eyes.

"That looked just like the brown head of Mrs. Beauty, but of course it wasn't," thought Peter. "I wish I could fly up and peek inside. I have had those Wood Ducks on my mind so much lately that I mistook someone else for Mrs. Beauty. I wish I could find out just who it is in there."

But Peter couldn't fly and he couldn't climb. The only thing he could do was to be patient and watch. He settled himself in comfort for watchful waiting. He sat there a long time, so long that finally he nodded and began to doze. At last he gave up.

71

"I'll come back tomorrow and watch all day if I have to," he decided. "If there is someone in there they'll have to come out sooner or later. I hope it will be sooner. That hole doesn't look big enough for even as small a Duck as Mrs. Beauty, but that did look like her head. But whoever heard of Ducks in a hollow tree?"

There are several kinds of Ducks that nest in holes in trees, but Peter didn't know that.

XI. What about the Babies?

Who for more knowledge never tries
Will never be accounted wise.

— PETER RABBIT

PETER WAS BACK under the little hemlock tree watching a hole in the tall dead tree standing a little way out in the water. It was the hole halfway up in that tree where he thought he had seen the head of Mrs. Beauty the Wood Duck. The more he thought about it the more he felt that he must have been mistaken, though how he could have been he couldn't see.

At last patience and persistence were rewarded, as usually they are. It was just after daybreak and he had been there only a short time when he heard a whistling. It was unlike any whistling but that made by swiftly moving wings and Peter knew that wings must be making it now. Then right before his eyes something happened that he never had thought to see. A bird alighted at that hole in the dead tree and whisked inside. This in itself wasn't surprising for he had seen many birds go into holes in trees. But this one was different. It was a Duck. Yes, sir, it was a Duck. There was no doubt about it, none at all.

"That was Mrs. Beauty!" exclaimed Peter. "So I wasn't mistaken yesterday. It must be that she is sitting in that old home of Logcock the Woodpecker. I wish she would come out where I can talk to her."

Mrs. Beauty didn't come out. Peter waited and waited and waited, but she didn't even so much as put her head out. At last he caught a glimpse of Beauty himself down the pond and close to shore. Away went Peter, lipperty-lipperty-lipperty-lip. He was quite out of breath when he got near enough to speak.

"I've found it!" cried Peter.

"That's nice. What is it?" replied the handsome little Duck as he preened his feathers.

"What is what?" asked Peter rather blankly.

"What is it you have found?" Beauty asked.

"Your secret, of course," declared Peter triumphantly.

"Have I a secret?" asked Beauty in a tone of surprise.

"You did have but you haven't now," cried Peter in triumph.

"You don't say! Where is it?" quacked Beauty, still pretending he didn't know what Peter meant.

74

"It is back there in the hollow in that dead tree standing in the water. That's where it is," cried Peter.

"It must be so if you say it is, but really I would like to know what it is," retorted Beauty.

Peter grinned. "What I want to know," said he, "is not what it is but how many it is. What's the use of pretending, Beauty? You know that I know where Mrs. Beauty is this very minute. You know that I know at last where that nest is. That is what I wanted to know at first, but now I want to know something more, and if you will tell me I promise I won't even tell Mrs. Peter."

"And just what is it you want to know?" inquired Beauty, as if he had no idea at all what Peter was talking about.

"How many eggs is Mrs. Beauty sitting on in that hollow tree? Don't tell me that she isn't sitting on any, for I know better. I saw her go in there, so it is useless for you to pretend that she isn't there. Now how many eggs has she?" replied Peter.

"Twelve," said Beauty promptly. "Yes, sir, she has twelve eggs up in that tree. We have had more than that in some years, but twelve is enough. When those eggs hatch we will have a family to be proud of. But for goodness sake, Peter, don't tell anyone where that nest is."

Of course Peter promised that he wouldn't, and he didn't. As usual he was full of questions. "Have you ever had your home in a hollow tree before?" he asked.

75

"We always nest in a hollow tree when we can find one. When Mrs. Beauty is sitting on her eggs she wants to be inside, not out in the open like most of our relatives. I was hatched in a hollow tree myself," explained Beauty.

"I suppose," said Peter, "that when you said at the Smiling Pool that you had found only one tree in all this part of the Green Forest that would do for your home it was because that was the only hollow tree you could find. Was that it?"

Beauty nodded. "Yes," said he, "that was it. At least, it is the only tree with a big enough hollow and a big enough doorway and up high enough to suit us."

"Do you always nest as high as that?" Peter wanted to know.

"No," said Beauty. "It all depends on what we can find. We have nested much higher than that, and we have nested in a hollow stump very near the ground. But the higher we are the safer we feel."

Peter scratched a long ear with a long hind foot. He was trying to scratch out a thought. He says he can think better that way. Beauty watched him a minute or two. "Well, Peter," said he at last, "what is it you have on your mind now?"

"Those baby Ducks you'll soon be having," replied Peter.

"What about those baby Ducks?" inquired Beauty.

"That hole is very high," said Peter.

"It would have suited us just as well had it been higher," replied Beauty.

"That is all very well for you and Mrs. Beauty, but what about the ducklings?" asked Peter.

"Well, what about them?" Beauty wanted to know.

"How," demanded Peter," are they ever going to get down to the water? Will you keep them up there until they are big enough to fly down? I can't imagine so many young Ducks big enough to fly being crowded into the hollow in that tree."

"Neither can I," chuckled Beauty. "I fear some of them would smother long before they were big enough to use their wings."

"Then how in the world will they get down?" cried Peter.

"They'll find a way, or we will find a way to get them down. You may be sure of that," said Beauty. "If you stick around you may have a chance to see how they get to the water."

"When will it be?" cried Peter eagerly.

"I don't know just when, but it won't be for sometime yet," replied Beauty. "You see it takes quite a while for Duck eggs to hatch, quite a while. Mrs. Beauty will be sitting on those eggs for quite a number of days yet."

"I'm going to stick around," said Peter.

Of course it would have made it much easier for Peter if Beauty had told him how many days Mrs. Beauty would be sitting on those eggs. Probably he didn't know himself. So Peter made frequent trips to the little pond to see if anything had happened or was happening. Each time he saw Beauty he admired him more.

"You are the handsomest bird I have ever seen," declared Peter, and really meant it.

"You flatter me," replied Beauty, but it was plain to see that he was pleased.

"And to think," said Peter, "that you were hatched from an egg in a hole on a tree!"

The pretty little Duck chuckled. "I believe something of the sort happened," said he.

"How did you get down to the water?" asked Peter artfully.

Again Beauty chuckled. "In one of the three ways that my ducklings may use," said he and there was a twinkle in his eyes.

"Three ways!" cried Peter. "Don't tell me that there are *three* ways! I don't see how there can be even one way."

"Just stick around and perhaps you'll see for yourself," quacked Beauty.

Peter sighed. Of course he couldn't stay there all the time. "It is mean of you not to tell me how it can be done. I hope I'll see it," said he.

"I hope you will. It is something to see," replied Beauty.

XII. The Little Unafraid Ones

How fortunate that in life's game
So few have talents just the same.
— PETER RABBIT

PETER RABBIT was in his favorite retreat under a little hemlock tree from where he could watch the Wood Duck home in the dead tree in the water. It was early in the morning and he had been out all night. So he was half asleep when he saw Mrs. Duck poke her head out of her doorway and look sharply all around. Her head was withdrawn and Peter was just about to yawn when she reappeared. This time she was holding something in her bill.

"Gracious!" exclaimed Peter, sitting up very straight. He was

79

no longer half asleep. He was very wide awake. Held in Mrs. Beauty's bill was one of her babies, a downy Duckling. In a twinkling she was out of her doorway and flying swiftly across the pond to the farther shore.

"Gracious!" exclaimed Peter again. "Did I really see that or did I dream it? I wonder if she will take the rest of them down that way."

He didn't wonder very long. Surprisingly soon Mrs. Beauty was back and inside that hollow high in the dead tree. She was working fast, was that pretty Mother Duck, for hardly had her tail disappeared inside when her head was thrust out again and as before she had a downy Duckling in her bill. Away she whirred on stout wings to the far shore. She was hiding her babies somewhere over there. Peter wished that he could be in two places at once. He wanted to stay where he was until the last of the Ducklings had left the nest, and he wanted to be over there on the other side to see where and how the mother was hiding her precious darlings.

"Oh dear! I wish there were two of me," he muttered.

For a few minutes he was undecided whether to remain where he was or to be satisfied with what he had already seen there and run around to where those ducklings were being taken.

"If I go over there I may not be able to find them and then I will miss out both ways. So I guess I will stay right here and see her carry the last one," he decided. Peter really does show a lot of sense at times.

As Mrs. Beauty came and went Peter tried to keep count of the ducklings, but soon he was all mixed up. "I don't see how I'm going to know when she gets the last one," thought he forlornly. "Hello! There she goes without one in her bill. I wonder if all are out and she came back to make sure."

Then he saw something that made him glad he had remained right where he was. Mother didn't have a duckling in her bill, but just the same she was carrying one. It was on her back. Yes, sir, that wee Duck was having a ride on his mother's back.

"I wouldn't have believed it if I hadn't seen it. No, sir, I wouldn't have believed it," Peter murmured.

In a few minutes Mrs. Beauty was back. A duckling was in the doorway waiting for her. He scrambled on her back and away he went for his first ride out in the Great World. Peter watched them until they were out of sight under some bushes on the other shore. Then he looked up again at that doorway in the dead tree. He was just in time to see a little downy bird with featherless little wings spread, come fluttering down splash into the water.

"Oh!" gasped Peter. "He fell out! What will he do?"

The duckling knew what to do. He was paddling about as if he thought it the most natural place in the world for him to be. It was too. Splash! Another had struck the water. Peter looked up just in time to see another come tumbling down, while behind in the doorway still another seemed to be getting ready to jump and didn't seem any more afraid to try it than those already down appeared to fear the water.

Just then Mother splashed into the water beside the ducklings, swam to each in turn, all the time talking to them softly, then flew up to the hole in the tree. She disappeared inside. She was gone but a moment. When she came out and flew down on the water she was alone. Peter guessed that she had gone up there to make sure that all were out. That they were Peter felt sure for now Mrs. Beauty started to swim slowly toward the other shore taking the little unafraid ones to join their brothers and sisters hidden over there. A prouder mother never was.

Peter watched them until they were out in the middle of the pond. Then he decided he would go around and try to find where the others had been hidden. Away he went, lipperty-lip-perty-lip. At the lower end of the pond was a dam which had been built by the Beaver folk and that made the pond. He started to cross on it. Halfway across he almost bumped into Beauty. Peter was in such a hurry that he hadn't looked as he should have to see where he was going. It might have been an enemy instead of the handsomest of all the Duck tribe. Beauty was taking a sun bath. He was almost half asleep.

"Why don't you look where you are going, Peter Rabbit?" he quacked crossly as Peter dodged around him.

"Excuse me," said Peter. "I didn't see you. Truly I didn't."

"You should have seen me. It is a lucky thing for you that I am who I am and not someone with a liking for a Rabbit dinner," retorted the Wood Duck.

"I know it," admitted Peter. "It was because I was hurrying so to see your family."

"My family? Have I a family?" asked Beauty.

"Don't you know that you have a family?" demanded Peter.

"No," replied Beauty. "No, I don't know anything about it. I know that Mrs. Beauty has been sitting on a lot of eggs. Have they hatched? You see I haven't been around here much lately."

"Where have you been?" Peter wanted to know at once.

"Oh, just loafing around with Mr. Quack and Mr. Sawbill, some of the time in this pond, some of the time in the other pond, some of the time down Laughing Brook in the pond of Slaptail the Beaver. If those eggs have hatched Mrs. Beauty probably has the youngsters up in that tree where the nest is," replied Beauty.

Peter shook his head and Beauty looked interested. "So they have left home already!" he exclaimed. "Did you see them leave?"

"I sure did," said Peter. "I told you I was going to stick around. And you were right about how they would get down. You said they might use one of three ways."

"So I did. Which way did they use?" said Beauty.

Peter chuckled. "Between them they used all three. Their mother took some down to the water in her bill and some on her back. The others tumbled down. Now Mrs. Beauty has them somewhere over on this other side of the pond and it was because I was in such a hurry to get around there and look for them that I almost ran into you," Peter explained.

"I think I will look myself," said Beauty. He waddled into the water and began to swim along shore.

Peter followed on the bank. They went quite a distance without seeing anything of Mrs. Beauty and the ducklings. That seemed queer to Peter, but Beauty didn't seem to think anything about it. He loafed along, stopping here and there. He seemed neither worried nor hurried. But his sharp eyes were not missing anything. By and by he stopped. He gave a low call. There was no answer. He called again. Still no answer. A moment or two later there was a rustling of dry leaves and from beneath some overhanging bushes appeared Mrs. Beauty. Twelve fluffy downy ducklings followed her into the water and all swam to meet Mr. Beauty.

A pretty sight they were, that trim little mother and her twelve babies. Beauty swam around them proudly. He had had no duties as a father. He felt no obligation of any duties now. But he certainly was proud of his family and he showed it.

As for Peter Rabbit, it seemed to him that never had he seen such a pretty family.

XIII. Mrs. Jerry Drops a Hint

The plainest facts some folks won't heed;
A hint is all some others need.

— OLD MOTHER NATURE

DAY AFTER DAY, night after night, Mrs. Quack the Mallard Duck had sat on her precious eggs in her nest in the grass and weeds on the roof of Paddy the Beaver's old house in the meadow in the Green Forest where Paddy had once had a pond. She had left those eggs only to get food. She didn't have to go far or stay long for that. In a little over three weeks those eggs hatched. Proudly Mrs. Quack led her babies down into the pool beside the old house and from this into Laughing Brook, which flows through the meadow. For a while they had stayed in the meadow. Mr. Quack had joined them there and then the whole family had gone on down Laughing Brook.

Of course it was a wonderful and exciting journey for the little Quacks. They spent several days in the pond of Slaptail the Beaver and then went on down to the Smiling Pool. Because of the cattails and flags and rushes growing in the shallow water at the head of it, and back of these a little swamp, the Smiling Pool is a favorite place with Mr. and Mrs. Quack. So the family spent several days there.

It had been a beautiful place to Mrs. Quack, but now it was a dreadful place. For her the Smiling Pool no longer smiled. Something dreadful had happened to two of her babies.

There never was a better or more watchful mother than Mrs. Quack. She never for one moment forgot to watch above for winged hunters with a taste for tender young ducks, or the shores for Reddy Fox and Bobby Coon and Billy Mink and other furry hunters with a taste for Ducks whether young or old. All her life she has had to watch for them and she has had more than one narrow escape. Still she does not hate them. That is because they hunt fairly and give those they hunt a chance.

"But what chance did those lost darlings have? And what chance did I have to warn them? None," said she bitterly to Mr. Quack. "We were all together when without warning one of the darlings was dragged down under water. To lose one

was bad enough, but a second was taken the same way. If we stay here we'll lose all of them, so — " She didn't finish. An ugly black head had appeared above water just a little way from them. It was the head of Snapper the Turtle.

Across the Smiling Pool and into Laughing Brook at the lower end the ducklings were hurried. Once there mother stopped hurrying and gathered her flock around her. "I hope," said she, "that all of you saw that ugly black head in the water."

All the ducklings nodded. "That was the head of Snapper the Turtle," she explained. "He and Mrs. Snapper are the most hateful enemies we Ducks have in or around the Smiling Pool."

"He didn't look dangerous," ventured one of the little ones.

"All you saw was his head. Had you seen how big he is you might think differently. You have wondered what happened to your lost brother and sister. That fellow could tell you. Either he or Mrs. Snapper came up beneath them and dragged them down to the bottom. Yes, my dears, that is what happened. And it could happen to all of you, and probably would if we were to go back to the Smiling Pool to stay." Mrs. Quack paused for breath.

"I guess that when we are as big as you we won't be afraid of those old Turtles," piped a small voice.

"If you are not afraid and are around where they are you won't be around long. I can tell you that. All wise Ducks, little or big, are afraid of them. Sometimes I think they must be the worst people in all the Great World," declared Mother Quack.

"If they live there all the time why hadn't we seen them before?" another duckling wanted to know.

"Because they seldom show themselves," replied his mother. "They spend most of their time in the mud at the bottom. They are hard to see even if you dive down close to them. They just lie there half buried, waiting for a fish or a Frog to swim within reach. Looking up they can see us Ducks swimming overhead. If they are hungry they just swim up and without warning grab one and drag him down to the bottom to eat. I guess everybody who lives in the Smiling Pool fears and hates those big Turtles. But Mr. and Mrs. Snapper don't seem to mind being hated. Now come on, Ducklings. We are going down to the Big River where we won't need to worry about those old Turtles."

In the water near the upper end of the Smiling Pool is the house of Jerry Muskrat. He and Mrs. Jerry have lived there a long time. This year Mrs. Jimmy Skunk had become a neighbor. She was living in an old underground house beneath the roots of a big hickory tree a little back from the edge of the bank where it was highest. She and Mrs. Jerry were on the best of terms. They never interfered with one another. While one lived on land and the other in the water they had one thing in common — mother love. Every evening as soon as the Black Shadows coming out from the Purple Hills reached the Smiling Pool Mrs. Jerry, watching from the roof of her house, would see a funny little procession come out from that underground house on the bank. First would come Mrs. Jimmy. Behind her would be her living image, only small, and following, one behind another, seven more in black coats with white stripes. Sometimes Mrs. Jimmy would lead them out on the Green Meadows to hunt for young Grasshoppers. Sometimes she would bring them down to play along the edge of the water while she and Mrs. Jerry gossiped as mothers will the world over.

Of course Mrs. Jimmy knew when the Quack family came down Laughing Brook to the Smiling Pool. She saw them for several days. Then she missed them. "I haven't seen the Quacks lately," said she to Mrs. Jerry one evening.

"They've left. They've gone down to the Big River. They didn't dare stay here any longer," squeaked Mrs. Jerry.

Mrs. Jimmy looked surprised and interested. "Who frightened them away? I haven't seen any visitors here of whom I would think they would be afraid," said she.

"It wasn't visitors who frightened them away. It was a couple of old settlers who probably have lived in the Smiling Pool longer than anyone else, and who show themselves so seldom that most folks forget they live here," squeaked Mrs. Jerry.

"I don't like riddles. Who are they?" grunted Mrs. Jimmy.

"Mr. and Mrs. Snapper. Those Turtles are bad actors. There was a time, when the children were smaller, that Jerry and I thought of leaving the Smiling Pool ourselves to take the youngsters where they would be safer. Now that they are big enough to have learned what the danger is and to watch for it I don't worry so much. Those Turtles are bigger and uglier than ever. I'm thankful they haven't a family growing up here," said Mrs. Jerry.

"You may thank some of your neighbors for that," replied Mrs. Jimmy with a sly grin.

"Who?" squeaked Mrs. Jerry.

"Myself for one. Jimmy too. And probably Bobby Coon," replied Mrs. Jimmy.

Mrs. Jerry looked puzzled. "What, may I ask, did you all have to do with it?" she wanted to know.

"We found Mrs. Snapper's eggs and ate them. So there were no little Snappers to grow up here in the Smiling Pool and make trouble," explained Mrs. Jimmy.

"Oh," said Mrs. Jerry.

"If you never have eaten Turtle eggs you have missed something," continued Mrs. Jimmy. "The Snappers, being the biggest of the Turtle cousins around here, have the biggest and best eggs. Speaking of them reminds me that it is about time to begin looking for eggs. Have you happened to see Mrs. Snapper go ashore lately?"

"No," replied Mrs. Jerry. "What would she be going ashore for?"

"To lay her eggs of course," replied Mrs. Jimmy a bit impatiently.

"How stupid of me! I forgot she goes ashore for that. It seems to me that I have heard that she buries them in the earth," said Mrs. Jerry.

Mrs. Jimmy nodded. "Right. That is just what she does," said she.

"And goes off and leaves them and never goes near them again?" questioned Mrs. Jerry.

Again Mrs. Jimmy nodded. "That is true too," she agreed.

"Then how does she know whether or not they hatch?" Mrs. Jerry wanted to know.

"She doesn't unless she sees some baby Turtles in the Smiling Pool. Then she doesn't know for sure that they are hers. I doubt if she ever thinks anything about it. If her eggs are found and eaten she never knows it," Mrs. Jimmy explained.

"She's a funny mother if you ask me," squeaked Mrs. Jerry.

"I don't call her a mother at all," declared Mrs. Jimmy.

Two nights later Mrs. Jerry told Mrs. Jimmy that very early that morning Mrs. Snapper had gone ashore and started off across the Green Meadows. It was a hint that Mrs. Jimmy wasn't slow to take.

XIV. Mrs. Snapper's Private Business

In other folks' affairs don't pry,
For no one really likes a spy.
— OLD MOTHER NATURE

PETER RABBIT had been out all night. You know he is one
of those folks who like to be out at night and sleep by day. This
doesn't mean he sleeps all day. Sometimes he is out and about
in the daytime just as you and I are sometimes out late in the
evening after being awake all day.

He was a little late this morning and anxious to get home to

94

the dear Old Briar-patch. He had been over in the Green Forest just looking around. He had come down along Laughing Brook to the Smiling Pool. Because he was late he didn't stop there, but started out across the Green Meadows, lipperty-lipperty-lipperty-lip. He always crosses the Green Meadows lipperty-lipperty-lipperty-lip, or almost always. He doesn't like to be out in the open in broad daylight.

Hardly had he left the Smiling Pool when he noticed a sort of path through the grass, the blades bent down and all pointing one way, out onto the Green Meadows. It could mean but one thing — that someone had been along there not long before. Peter stopped. He looked ahead across the Green Meadows. He looked back to the Smiling Pool. He saw no one. Who had been along there and bent that grass down?

Peter forgot that he was in a hurry. He forgot that he was out in the open, not a safe place for any Rabbit to be in broad daylight. He just *had* to know who had left the Smiling Pool to go out on the Green Meadows, why they had done it and what had become of them. He just *had* to know. Curiosity always is like that. So Peter started to follow that sort of path of bent grass.

He didn't run now. He would hop a few steps then sit up to look. Whoever had been along there seemed to be going nowhere in particular. The path didn't lead straight in any direction; it wandered about.

"Somebody didn't know where they were going, or else were

looking for something," thought Peter. He became more curious than ever. Nothing grows faster than curiosity.

At last, sitting up for a look ahead, he thought the grass ahead of him moved a little. He stared long and hard. Yes, it did move! And it wasn't wind that was making it move for not a single Merry Little Breeze had yet reached the Green Meadows. Someone hidden by the tall grass was pushing through it and making it move. It had to be that.

Now Peter moved on more carefully. He wanted to find out who he was following before getting too near. That was just good, plain common sense, and Peter does have a little of it even though he is happy-go-lucky. Not far ahead was a place where the grass was short and thin. The ground there was too sandy for anything to grow well.

Out from the tall grass around the sandy place was thrust a black head with a pair of beady eyes and the ugliest-looking horny jaws you can imagine. Peter sat very still. That black head kept very still. After what seemed a very long time to Peter the biggest Turtle he ever had seen slowly walked out. It was Mrs. Snapper the Snapping Turtle.

"Oh!" said Peter, and made a couple of hops nearer.

Perhaps Mrs. Snapper heard him. Anyway she stopped, drew her legs close to her sides, and drew her head back. She couldn't draw it into her shell in the manner of most of the Turtle cousins for unlike them she has only a small under shell. There is no shell to draw her head back into.

As she lay there on the ground without moving she looked

much like a big, nearly flat, moss-covered stone. She had lived so long in the Smiling Pool, spending most of her time in the mud at the bottom, that moss had grown on her upper shell. Lying there without moving she looked harmless. No one as slow as she could be dangerous. Anyway that is what Peter thought.

He hopped nearer and stared most impolitely. Suddenly Mrs. Snapper was on her feet. Her head and an astonishingly long neck shot out at Peter so quickly that he barely saw the movement. Luckily for him those horny jaws didn't reach him. They just barely missed him. He made a frantic jump to safety, then turned to stare at the big Turtle.

She stared back and those beady eyes gave him a most uncomfortable feeling. She opened her mouth and hissed at him. He saw the sharp edges of her horny jaws that could have snapped off one of his legs with a single bite had they reached him. He knew then how lucky, how very lucky, it was that he had been no nearer when she had struck at him. Watching her plodding through the tall grass he had thought her the slowest person he ever had seen. Now he knew she could shoot out her head and snap together those wicked-looking jaws as quickly as Buzztail the Rattlesnake can strike, and that is almost too quickly for the eye to follow.

"Never again will I get so near her. No, sir, I never will," thought Peter. Then, as politely as he knew how, he asked her where she was going.

"Is that any business of yours?" hissed Mrs. Snapper.

Of course it wasn't and Peter knew it wasn't. So he said nothing, just sat there waiting and watching. When she did move on he wondered if she knew herself where she was going. She wandered about as if looking for something rather than going somewhere in particular. She stopped and seemed to do something with her feet, then went on. Peter, following, found that she had scratched away a little grass and sand. She did this several times. It was as if she had started to dig, then changed her mind.

At last in a place where the ground was slightly damp but in a sunny spot she once more stopped. Peter stopped too, far enough back of her so that she did not see him when she looked around. In a few minutes he saw her kick with one of her stout hind feet. A little grass and sand flew out behind her. She did the same thing with the other hind foot. She had begun to dig a hole. Yes, sir, that is just what she was doing, and she was doing it with her *hind* feet.

She would loosen the earth with the claws of one foot, then kick it out. Then with the other foot she would repeat. It seemed to Peter a funny way to dig a hole. In the first place she couldn't see what she was doing. But this didn't seem to bother her. She kept right at work, this foot, that foot, this foot, that foot, never once looking behind or to one side. She had a job to do and she was doing it. She would keep right on doing it until it was finished.

Peter moved a little nearer. She paid no attention to him. She kept right on digging — left foot, right foot, left foot, right foot. The hole steadily grew a little deeper and a little bigger. It was a slanting sort of hole. Her tail and hind feet disappeared in it, but her head and front feet remained outside. By and by she stopped digging. For some time she seemed to be busy, but what she was doing Peter didn't know and couldn't see. He wanted to go nearer but didn't dare do that. Not even to satisfy curiosity would he risk a bite from those sharp-edged jaws. No sir!

After a time Mrs. Snapper lifted herself a little and with a hind foot raked in some of the earth she had dug out. He had just a glimpse of something white in the hole.

"Eggs!" thought Peter. "That is her nest and she has almost filled it with eggs! I wonder what she will do now."

He soon found out. Mrs. Snapper raked in the sand she had dug out, still using her hind feet. She filled the hole and raked the loose sand and other material over it so that should anyone pass that way they would not be likely to notice the place. In a day or two it would be quite like the surroundings. Then with not even one backward glance Mrs. Snapper headed back for the Smiling Pool and it was plain that she was in a hurry to get there. There was no wandering about now. She knew where the Smiling Pool was and she took the shortest way straight there.

She hadn't even seen her eggs. Now that they were safely buried in the right kind of a place that was damp enough and where Mr. Sun could keep them warm enough she had no more interest in them. She had done her duty and she didn't care what might happen to those eggs. If at the end of several weeks they should hatch the babies would find their own way to the Smiling Pool and there look out for themselves, not even knowing that they had a mother.

Peter suddenly recalled where he was and that he should have been home long ago. Off he went, lipperty-lipperty-lip, to the dear Old Briar-patch to tell Mrs. Peter what had kept him so long.

XV. Mrs. Jimmy Takes Over

Be slow to boast lest in the end
Humiliation shall attend.
— OLD MOTHER NATURE

AS PETER RABBIT hurried home to the dear Old Briar-patch after watching Mrs. Snapper bury her eggs he did not suspect that a pair of keen, crafty eyes had watched him from a distance. The eyes were those of Reddy Fox. From the Old Pasture Reddy had watched Peter but had not tried to catch him. For one thing it was a very warm June morning, much too warm to do any hard running. For another thing it was doubtful if he could get near enough to Peter without being seen to stand a chance of catching him before he could reach the safe Old Briar-patch. Reddy is much too smart to do useless running, especially on such a warm morning.

But he has his share of curiosity. "Longears over there is watching something or someone," said Reddy to himself. "I wonder what or who it is to make him forget that he is right out in plain sight when he should be at home in that pesky Old Briar-patch. When I start out hunting this evening I'll look around over there where he is now." He yawned and curled up for a sun bath and nap.

When the Black Shadows crept across the Green Meadows that evening Reddy went along with them. At the place where he had seen Peter sitting that morning he sniffed here and he sniffed there, trying to find Peter's scent. But the day had been long and bright without enough dampness to hold Peter's scent save for just a wee bit here and there, not enough for Reddy to follow.

But his eyes are as good as his nose. They didn't miss the bent grass where Mrs. Snapper had come from and returned to the Smiling Pool. "So that was it! That old Turtle was up here to dig a nest and lay her eggs and Peter saw her doing it," thought he, and began to look around carefully.

"I wouldn't mind finding those eggs," said he, talking to himself. "There should be quite a number of them. Turtles are queer folks. They bury their eggs and then forget them. Hello! Here comes someone else looking for eggs or I miss my guess. I should have come earlier."

Sure enough, someone was coming. It was Bobby Coon. He had been hunting Frogs at the Smiling Pool. That is one of his favorite occupations. Frogs are one of his favorite foods and hunting them is a lot of fun. Prowling along the edge of the Smiling Pool he had found where Mrs. Snapper had entered the water on her return from laying her eggs and he had guessed what she had been doing.

"So Mrs. Snapper has been out on the Green Meadows and I know why. I had forgotten that this is the time for Turtle eggs. A dinner of eggs would be even better than a dinner of Frogs. I think I will look around out there a bit. I would like some of those eggs. I would so," said he, and licked his lips.

Now when Mrs. Snapper had returned to the Smiling Pool she had come straight from her nest to the water, leaving a trail of bent grass easy to follow. Bobby Coon had no trouble at all in following it back to where it started. When he saw Reddy Fox he paid no attention to him. In the first place he was bigger and much heavier than Reddy. In the second place he was a famous fighter and he knew that Reddy knew it and was far too wise to pick a quarrel. So he pretended not to see Reddy and went about the business of searching for a soft place in the ground. Presently he found it.

At once Bobby began to dig. He had dug out only a little earth when out rolled a round white egg. Bobby picked it up in his black hands, looked over at Reddy and grinned, then popped that egg into his mouth. He ate it. He pulled out another and ate that. All the time Reddy Fox looked on, his mouth watering as he tried to think of some way to get some of those eggs.

Bobby Coon was selfish. There were many eggs but he had no intention of sharing them. He intended to have every egg in that nest. So he settled himself to the pleasant task of pulling out those eggs and eating them. As he pulled out his fifth egg he was startled by the stamping of feet close at hand. Even before he looked up he knew what to expect. There, close at hand, stood Mrs. Jimmy Skunk stamping her black forefeet in a manner that couldn't be mistaken. She meant business, and when Jimmy or Mrs. Jimmy mean business everyone gets out of their way. Bobby did now and he did it in such a hurry that he dropped the egg he had just pulled out of Mrs. Snapper's nest.

Bobby backed away in a hurry but he didn't back far enough to suit Mrs. Jimmy. She took a few quick steps toward him and stamped again. Her big tail was held high. Bobby knew what that meant. It was a warning. It was a danger signal. All the people of the Green Forest and the Green Meadows know that signal and, big and little, all heed it. Bobby Coon did now. He turned and ran a short distance and Bobby was three times the size of Mrs. Jimmy.

While this was going on Reddy Fox thought he saw an opportunity and Reddy isn't one to knowingly miss an opportunity. He is an opportunist by nature. He darted toward those eggs. Just before he was near enough to get one Mrs. Jimmy turned. She stamped. There was a threat in that stamping. Reddy turned and ran away faster than he had come. Mrs. Jimmy stamped again, then settled herself comfortably beside

the eggs, pulled one out and ate it. She had taken over and there was nothing that Reddy Fox, or Bobby Coon, or the two together could do about it. Mrs. Jimmy always is prepared and everybody knows it and respects her.

"Those eggs are mine," snarled Bobby Coon.

Mrs. Jimmy said nothing, merely reached in that hole and pulled out another round white egg and ate it.

"I found them," growled Bobby.

"I've got them," said Mrs. Jimmy, and reached for another.

At a safe distance Bobby Coon walked back and forth uneasily, growling threats. Mrs. Jimmy paid them no attention. Bobby was so big that compared with him Mrs. Jimmy looked small although she was large for a Skunk.

"I could kill you," snarled Bobby. He wasn't boasting. He was so big and strong that in a fight he could do that without much trouble and he knew it.

"But think how unpleasant it would be," barked Reddy Fox and grinned.

Mrs. Jimmy paid no more attention to either of them than if they had not been there. Calmly, without hurry, she pulled out those eggs and ate them. Bobby Coon edged nearer and nearer. Once he stood up on his hind feet the way Buster Bear does. He was trying to look into that hole to see how many eggs were left. Mrs. Jimmy turned her back to him.

Bobby dropped back on all four feet and moved a little nearer. Without warning Mrs. Jimmy whirled about and her big bushy tail flew up. She stamped hard. It had a threatening sound. In his haste to get away Bobby almost fell over backward. Mrs. Jimmy made a short run at him. Bobby showed her his black heels and this time he kept on going. He had abruptly decided that he preferred Frogs to eggs.

"Did I hear you say that those eggs are yours?" barked Reddy Fox and chuckled.

Unhurriedly Mrs. Jimmy returned to the eggs in the ground. She ate and ate. At a short distance but a respectful distance Reddy Fox sat watching her. His mouth watered so that he drooled. Yes, sir, he drooled. Would she eat all of those eggs? If she didn't would she go away, or would she stay around until she became hungry again?

After a while she ate more slowly. She would pull an egg out and let it lie for a few minutes, or roll it about under her black paws before eating it. Now and then she would stop and lick her lips. Reddy Fox, watching her, would lick his lips too.

Now enough is enough, and wise is he who knows it and acts accordingly. There were more eggs than Mrs. Jimmy could eat for one meal. When she had eaten her fill she unhurriedly ambled back toward the underground home beneath the roots of the big hickory tree near the Smiling Pool and the babies waiting there for her.

Four eggs were left. So Reddy Fox had a taste that he felt was worth waiting for. In the fall no baby Snapping Turtles made their way to the Smiling Pool to add to the worries of the people living there. It was just as well.

XVI. A Laughing Brook Big Family

The right to live is given all
However big, however small.
— OLD MOTHER NATURE

THE HOME OF CHATTERER the Red Squirrel is in the Green Forest and it is there that he spends most of his time. Only once in a while does he leave it to run over to the Old Orchard. He had built his nest high in an oak tree near Laughing Brook and there was little going on in that part of the Green Forest that he didn't see or know about. Laughing Brook has many visitors. Many come to it to drink. Some come to it to bathe. A few travel up and down it between the Big River and the Great Mountain. And many visit it to catch fish.

Of late he had heard a lot of complaining. Farmer Brown's boy had come up Laughing Brook fishing. There were some nice pools for Trout in that part of Laughing Brook and Farmer Brown's boy had fished them patiently and carefully. He had caught nothing and as he went away he was talking to himself. Chatterer couldn't understand his words but he understood perfectly his tone of voice. He was complaining because he had caught no fish.

Hardly was he out of sight when Billy Mink appeared. He too was fishing, and he too was feeling out of sorts.

"Hello, Billy Mink! What luck?" called Chatterer from a limb that overhung Laughing Brook. He felt quite safe there should Billy Mink turn hunter instead of fisherman.

"No luck," grumbled Billy. "Never have I known such poor fishing. I used to be able to catch plenty without half trying, but now this brook seems to be fished out."

The next day who should appear shuffling along Laughing Brook, sometimes in the water and sometimes on the bank, but Buster Bear. In his deep, rumbly, grumbly voice he was muttering to himself.

"Such fishing! Such fishing!" grumbled Buster. "What has become of all the fish? I wonder if Little Joe Otter and Billy Mink have caught them all."

"I don't know about Little Joe Otter. I haven't seen him

around for a long time. But Billy Mink isn't to blame. He was along here yesterday complaining of the poor fishing and wondering what has become of the fish," said Chatterer.

When, still grumbling, Buster Bear had gone on Peter Rabbit came out of a hollow log in which he had been hiding. "Buster doesn't seem very happy," said he.

"It is because he isn't having good fishing," replied Chatterer.

"He isn't the only one," said Peter. "Rattles the Kingfisher is about ready to stop fishing in the Smiling Pool. Longlegs the Heron says that were it not for Pollywogs and Frogs he would starve if he had to depend on the Smiling Pool and Laughing Brook for food. I wonder what has become of the fish."

A few days later Peter was sitting under a fern by a pool that was deep and dark and cool, the kind of a pool that Trout love. Close to it was a big flat rock. Happening to look over to it Peter saw a head appear over the farther edge. Out of the water onto the rock glided a member of the Snake family, one of the biggest he ever had seen. It was Mrs. Water Snake. Peter wasn't afraid of her for he was much too big for her to pay any attention to. So he continued to sit there under the fern.

Mrs. Water Snake took a long sun bath. At last she began to move. She slid over the edge of the rock into the pool and Peter thought he had seen the last of her. He was mistaken. A moment or two later she glided up on the rock again. In her mouth was a nice Trout. She began to swallow it head first. Slowly it disappeared.

"I'm glad I don't have to swallow my food that way," thought Peter. "I don't see what fun there can be in eating. My, my, look at her mouth stretch! Just watching her makes my jaws ache."

The Trout disappeared down Mrs. Water Snake's throat and she once more basked in the sun. Peter noticed that she lay with her head close to the edge of the rock where she could look down in the pool. It wasn't long before she glided into the water again. Once more she brought a Trout, a smaller one, out on the rock and swallowed it.

"She certainly likes fish," thought Peter. Then it popped into Peter's head that perhaps he had found out one reason for the scarcity of fish in Laughing Brook. In just the short time he had been watching her that Snake had caught and swallowed two. If there were many of her kind along Laughing Brook it was no wonder that fish were getting scarce, no wonder at all.

"It seems to me that I have heard that Water Snakes have large families. If that is so it must take a lot of fish to feed the young Snakes after they are big enough to catch fish. Because they are so seldom seen fishing I suppose those Snakes could get most of the fish in a brook without anyone knowing it, and others would get the blame." Peter was very close to the truth.

He knew that Longlegs the Heron was blaming Rattles the Kingfisher, Rattles was blaming Billy Mink, and Billy was blaming Farmer Brown's boy and other two-legged fishermen for the poor fishing in the Smiling Pool and Laughing Brook.

It always is easy to blame the other fellow. But Peter was sure that not one of them was wholly to blame.

"It is Mrs. Water Snake and others of her kind," thought Peter.

A few days later he was back under the fern by the pool where he had seen Mrs. Water Snake, hoping to see her again. For a long time the big flat rock beside the pool remained bare. It was very quiet there. Nothing happened. Peter began to doze. Finally he took a short nap.

When he opened his eyes at last and looked over at that flat rock he thought he must still be asleep and dreaming, and no wonder. What he saw was hard to believe. Yes, sir, it was hard to believe. On that flat rock Mrs. Water Snake was taking a sun bath, but she wasn't alone. That rock was covered with Snakes, little Snakes. They were crawling all over it and over Mrs. Water Snake and over each other. Never had Peter seen so many Snakes at one time.

His eyes were open their widest as he looked on. "Goodness!" he gasped. "Can it be possible that that is all one family? That all those little Snakes belong to Mrs. Water Snake? It doesn't seem possible that any mother can have so many children at one time. No, sir, it doesn't seem possible. If I didn't see it I wouldn't believe it. I wonder how many of those babies there are."

But Peter didn't count them. He couldn't. They didn't keep still long enough to be counted. No one could have counted them because after a minute or two it would be impossible to tell which had been counted and which hadn't. So it is no wonder that he was discouraged. As a matter of fact there were nearly fifty. Water Snakes often have as many, or more than that number. They believe in big families. Mrs. Water Snake was very big herself. Perhaps that is the reason she had such an extra big family.

Chatterer the Red Squirrel happened along. Peter saw him. "Do you remember," said Peter, "how Billy Mink and Buster Bear complained because the fishing was so poor?"

"Yes," said Chatterer. "What about it?"

"I think I know the reason," replied Peter.

"Well, what is the reason?" demanded Chatterer.

"Look over on that flat rock. You'll see the reason and a lot of little reasons," said Peter and grinned.

Chatterer looked. He saw Mrs. Water Snake and her family. "What have they to do with fish?" he demanded.

Before Peter could reply Mrs. Water Snake slid into the water. A moment later she was back on the flat rock in the midst of her babies. In her mouth was a small Trout. This she slowly swallowed. Chatterer said nothing. He knew now what Peter meant.

"Have you ever seen so many children in one family?" Peter asked.

"Yes," replied Chatterer, "I've seen more. I have seen little Mrs. Garter Snake with a bigger family than that." And he really had.

"I don't believe it," declared Peter, then hastily added, "If you

113

say it is so of course it is so. When all those little Snakes on that rock are bigger what a lot of fish it will take to feed them."

"True," replied Chatterer. "And all the time other folks will be blamed for taking too many fish. But that's the way it goes in this world. Too often the wrong people are blamed for bad things that are done. Well, I don't like Snakes and I'm not going to stay here."

"Neither am I," said Peter. With this both scampered away.

XVII. The Confusion of Peter

This saying you'll find true though trite:
It always pays to be polite.

— PETER RABBIT

LIKE A LOT OF OTHER PEOPLE Peter Rabbit is given to making positive statements about things of which he knows little or nothing. The world is full of Peter Rabbits. At times they make a lot of trouble without meaning to.

Peter had discovered that Mrs. Quack's children could swim almost as soon as they were out of their shells. He didn't think so much of their running about. He knew of other babies who could run almost at once, the babies of Mrs. Grouse, Mrs. Woodcock and Mrs. Bob White. But swimming was another matter, something to be learned it seemed to him.

He was watching them when Teeter the Spotted Sandpiper lighted at the edge of the water near him and teetered and bobbed in that funny manner of his as if trying to keep his balance on his slim legs. "Those babies could swim the day they were hatched," said Peter.

"What of it?" asked Teeter, bobbing up and down.

"Why, they didn't have to learn. I guess Duck babies are the only ones who can run about and swim the first day. It is wonderful," replied Peter.

"What is wonderful about that? I know of babies who can do more than run and swim the first day," declared Teeter, still bobbing as if trying to keep his balance.

"What else can they do?" demanded Peter.

"They can dive," said Teeter.

"I don't believe it," snapped Peter most impolitely.

"What you do or do not believe doesn't make the least bit of difference. They can do it and will do it just the same," retorted Teeter.

"Are you telling me that you know of babies who can run, swim and dive the day they are born?" demanded Peter.

"I've told you," retorted Teeter.

"Then tell me whose babies they are," demanded Peter.

"Mine," was Teeter's wholly unexpected reply. It made Peter blink, the more so because he didn't know whether to believe it

116

or not. Teeter flew away before Peter could ask more questions.

It really was hard to believe. Teeter is a shore bird, not a water bird. For his size his legs are long, running legs. His feet are not webbed like a Duck's. How could his babies swim and dive?

The next day Peter was back at Laughing Brook looking for Teeter. Along the edge of the water a slim, trim little bird with a long bill was running, stopping every few steps to pick up something, then stand for a moment bobbing and bowing and teetering in the funniest manner.

"Hi, Teeter! Did you really mean all you told me yesterday?" cried Peter.

"What did I tell you?" was the unexpected reply.

"Why, you know. You said your babies can run, swim and dive the very first day," said Peter.

"No, I didn't. I didn't tell you anything of the kind. I didn't even see you yesterday," replied his small neighbor.

Peter blinked rather stupidly. "Why Teeter, how can you say such a thing?" he cried.

"Because it is true. And do stop calling me Teeter. I'm Mrs. Teeter," was the prompt retort. It made Peter blink more than ever.

"Oh," said he lamely as he watched Mrs. Teeter fly a little way and then light on a rock out on the water where she teetered and bobbed and bowed as only a Spotted Sandpiper can.

"I never before realized how alike Mr. and Mrs. Teeter look," muttered Peter as he squatted under a fern to think things over.

"I wonder how many times I have made that mistake before. How in the world can anyone tell them apart? Perhaps Mrs. Teeter can tell me."

He crept from under the fern and looked for Mrs. Teeter where he had last seen her. Then he hurried along the shore until he was opposite that rock to which she had flown. "Excuse me, Mrs. Teeter, for that mistake I made. You look so like Teeter that I thought you were him. If I didn't know better I would make the same mistake right over again now," said he.

"So you think I look exactly like Teeter, do you? I suspect I do. I ought to. It would be strange if I didn't," was the surprising reply.

Peter stared. "Why would it?" he demanded.

"Because I am Teeter. Mrs. Teeter is over yonder. She left this rock and I came to it while you were under that fern," explained Teeter, for Teeter it was.

Just then Mrs. Teeter joined Teeter on the rock and the two stood bobbing and bowing side by side. Peter stared. It was very confusing. "However am I to tell you apart?" he cried.

"Does it matter?" asked Teeter.

A week later Peter was over by the Smiling Pool running, lipperty-lipperty-lip, in his usual heedless happy-go-lucky way when someone flew up almost in his face. It startled him so that he leaped to one side, then stopped and turned to see what had happened. Facing him was a thoroughly angry small person threatening to pick his eyes out, and demanding to know why

118

he didn't watch his step and look where he was going. Then Peter saw the cause of all this fuss. On the ground where the grass grew thinly and there were many pebbles scattered about was a slight hollow in the sand. It was lined with a little grass and in this nest were four spotted eggs that looked much like the surrounding pebbles.

"I'm ever so sorry, Mrs. Teeter. I had no idea you had a nest anywhere around here or I would have been more careful," said Peter.

"You are the most heedless fellow I know. It is a good thing I was at home or you probably would have stepped right on those eggs and broken them," scolded the little Sandpiper.

"That would have been too bad. But you could have laid some more," said Peter.

"No such thing. I couldn't have laid more," retorted the angry little bird.

"Why not? I've known other birds to do that when something happened to their first eggs," said Peter.

"Because I don't lay eggs," was the sharp retort.

"You don't lay eggs!" cried Peter. "What in the world do you mean, Mrs. Teeter?"

"Just what I said, and for goodness sake stop calling me Mrs. Teeter. Just because we happen to look alike, and I am a good fellow around home, is no reason why I should be mistaken for her," protested Teeter, for Teeter it was.

Peter apologized. "I'm sorry," said he. "Anyway Mrs. Teeter could have laid some more eggs."

"Small chance," retorted Teeter. "She isn't around and I don't know where she is. She isn't domestic. Family cares bore her. So she goes off and has a good time. And that's that."

"Do you mean you do all the sitting on the eggs?" asked Peter.

"Yes, and I take all the care of the babies. Who would if I didn't?" replied Teeter.

"My goodness, I don't know what I would do if Mrs. Peter should leave all the care of our babies to me!" exclaimed Peter.

"I know what the babies would do," said Teeter drily.

"What?" asked Peter.

"Die," replied Teeter.

A few days later Peter was over by the Big River. On the shore he met Mrs. Teeter. He knew it was she because Teeter was patiently sitting on those eggs. "I should think you would be ashamed of yourself," said Peter severely.

Mrs. Teeter looked surprised. "Why should I be ashamed?" she demanded.

"For leaving all your household cares to Teeter," said Peter.

"Oh that!" exclaimed Mrs. Teeter. "I don't care for that sort of thing, and he doesn't mind."

"But he will have all the care of the babies. What kind of a mother are you anyway?" cried Peter.

"As good a mother as you are a father," retorted Mrs. Teeter, and to that Peter had nothing to say, for he has nothing to do with the care of his own babies.

Mrs. Teeter flew off down the Big River. Peter watched her out of sight. He shook his head. "A funny mother, if you ask me," said he. Then he decided he would go see how Teeter was getting along. When he reached the place where he had so nearly stepped on those precious eggs he found neither eggs nor babies nor Teeter himself.

XVIII. The Precocious Babies

The children who grow up are they
Who heed their elders and obey.
— OLD MOTHER NATURE

IT WAS FUNNY. Yes, sir, it was funny. No wonder Peter Rabbit chuckled as he watched. On a flat stone at the edge of the water at the upper end of the Smiling Pool was one of the cutest babies in all the Great World. From where Peter was peeping from beneath a big fern that baby looked like little more than a small pinch of soft down on legs as small as toothpicks. It was so tiny and so young, less than two days old, that it was hard to believe that it could stand, let alone walk and run. Yet as

Peter well knew those little legs had brought the downy mite from a nest which to one so small must seem a long distance from where he now was.

"Without making a sound he is telling all who happen to see him whose baby he is," chuckled Peter.

The midget was gravely bobbing and bowing *backward,* if you please. Instead of bowing with his head he was bowing with the other end of his body. Anyway that is how it looked. No wonder Peter chuckled.

"Peet-weet! Peet-weet!" came a call from across the water. On the opposite shore Peter saw Teeter running at the water's edge and stopping to bob and bow *backward* as is his way. No one seeing him and then looking at that baby bobbing and bowing on the flat rock would have any doubt about whose baby it was.

Peter was wondering if he could get nearer to the tiny Sandpiper without frightening him when there came a sharp call from across the Smiling Pool. He knew it for what it was, the Sandpiper danger call. He looked over just in time to see Teeter take wing and disappear up Laughing Brook. He looked back at the flat stone on which the baby had been. There was no baby there. As he turned he had caught a glimpse of a swiftly moving form flying low and disappearing up Laughing Brook. He knew it was Sharpshin the Hawk.

"So that's it," muttered Peter. "Teeter saw him coming and gave warning, but it was just too late. Sharpshin must have grabbed that baby while I was watching Teeter. It is too bad. Yes, sir, it is too bad. That little fellow didn't live long. It is a wonder to me that any babies live to grow up. When I think of all the dangers, all the hungry hunters watching for them day and night, I don't see how any of them manage to live. I don't see how I did myself. Goodness knows even now I have trouble enough keeping alive. That baby was so small that he couldn't have made more than a bite for Sharpshin and a small one at that. I wonder what has become of the others. There were four eggs in that nest but when I last saw it the babies had left it. I wonder if Sharpshin got all of them."

Having nothing to do and being well hidden Peter continued to sit right where he was. He would doze for a moment or two, open his eyes, then doze again. It was after one of these short naps that he looked at that flat stone again. He wondered if he really was awake. On that stone, bobbing and bowing, was that baby Sandpiper.

"Peet-weet," called Teeter.

At once the downy mite left the flat stone and ran to join his father. Then from another direction another baby ran toward Teeter. "Peet-weet," called Teeter again. It seemed to Peter as if a little stone, one among many out in front, came to life, jumped up and ran to answer that call. Of course nothing like that really happened. That wee Sandpiper lying flat among those stones and keeping perfectly still had looked so like a stone that Peter had mistaken him for one.

"Too, too bad," thought Peter, "that Sharpshin caught that other one." Then he blinked and counted the babies with Teeter. He counted again. Unless something was wrong with his eyes four tiny Sandpipers were running about near Teeter and picking up food. Peter crept out from under the fern and slowly hopped over to the busy family. Teeter and Peter are old friends. Because Teeter wasn't afraid the babies were not afraid.

"When I saw the eggs in your nest I saw only four. Did Mrs. Teeter lay another?" asked Peter.

"No," said Teeter. "Don't you see that there are but four of these little scamps?"

"But Sharpshin the Hawk caught one," cried Peter.

"Your mistake," replied Teeter. "I gave the hide call. That scamp you thought was caught was flat among the stones before that Hawk got there, so he wasn't seen."

"But he isn't two days old! How did he know what to do and how to do it?" cried Peter.

"I guess it is born in them," replied Teeter. "Watch." He gave the alarm signal. As if by magic the busy mites disappeared. They did it instantly and completely. Not one waited a second to find out what or where the danger might be.

"Born in them is right," said Peter as he tried in vain to tell them from the stones among which they were lying flat.

"Peet-weet, Peet-weet," called Teeter again and up popped the four and began bobbing and bowing and running about just as if they hadn't been hiding at all.

126

"It is hard to believe," said Peter.

"What is hard to believe?" asked Teeter.

"That babies not two days old should be so smart," replied Peter.

"They learn fast. They must or they won't live long. And they have a lot to learn. Yes, sir, they have a lot to learn. But if they remember the first and most important lesson I won't worry too much about them," said Teeter.

"And what, may I ask, is that?" said Peter wonderingly.

"Obedience," replied Teeter, and emphasized it by bobbing more than ever. "You saw them disappear the instant I gave the signal."

"No," said Peter, "I didn't see them disappear. If I had I would have seen just where they went."

"Not one waited," continued Teeter just as if Peter hadn't spoken. "That was a signal to hide, and they hid. They didn't ask why or stop to look around. Instant obedience is the first important lesson in life for all children. Often it saves their lives. And it saves their parents a lot of worry. Don't you agree?"

Peter nodded gravely, quite as if he knew all about it. The truth is Peter leaves all the care of his children to Mrs. Peter and doesn't worry about them at all. Just then one of the wee Sandpipers ran to the edge of the water and stopped with his toes in it. Then he waded in. In a jiffy he was beyond his depth and afloat.

"Oh!" cried Peter.

Teeter was not at all disturbed. "I thought he would be trying the water pretty soon," said he.

Another waded in. "Look, they are swimming!" cried Peter.

"I should hope so," said their father. "It would be just too bad if they couldn't swim."

"But how can they? When did they learn? Who taught them? They are not two days old yet," cried Peter.

"What of it?" retorted Teeter.

"But — but — but —" began Peter.

"But nothing," interrupted Teeter. "They didn't need to learn to swim any more than baby Ducks need to. They didn't have to learn to swim any more than they had to learn to run. They just walked in and swam. You saw them."

"Is it the first time they ever have been in the water?" Peter wanted to know.

"The very first," replied Teeter. "And," he added, "it may be the last time if they go too far out or too near those lily pads." He called softly and at once the wee swimmers came ashore.

Peter looked over the Smiling Pool. There wasn't so much as a ripple on its smooth surface. He looked over to the lily pads. No one was to be seen. He looked all around in the sky for Sharpshin or some other Hawk. None was in sight.

"What were you afraid of? What would have happened to them if they had gone farther out or over to those lily pads?" he asked.

128

"Perhaps nothing would have happened to them, but some-thing could. I don't know which would like most one or both of them for dinner, Snapper the Turtle or Grandfather Frog."

"Oh," said Peter, remembering what had happened to two of Mrs. Quack's Ducklings. "I hadn't thought of them."

XIX. Teeter Wins Respect

Do something others cannot do
And they will have respect for you.

— OLD MOTHER NATURE

IT IS TRUE. The quickest, surest way to get the respect of others is to do something they cannot do. What you may do is a small matter if you alone can do it. It may be something useful, daring, skilful or none of these things. As long as others cannot do it it will win a certain amount of respect.

Ever since his first visit to the Smiling Pool long ago Peter Rabbit had been acquainted with Teeter the Spotted Sandpiper. Teeter was an old friend. I suspect that Peter would have said that he knew all about Teeter and his ways. Of course he didn't. He was finding this out now. There is no more common mistake in all the Great World than for one to think he knows all about his neighbors.

"I have always thought of you Sandpipers as land birds, not water birds," said Peter. He had been watching two of Teeter's babies swim.

"Peet-weet! Peet-weet! We are land birds," replied Teeter. "We are land birds who love to be near the water. We get most of our food there. There are many other birds who also live along the water's edge, the shores of rivers, ponds, lakes and the Great Ocean. So we are called shore birds. Shore birds are land birds who love to be close to the water. Do you see?"

Peter thought it over for a minute. "I see," said he.

"So, loving the water, we are not afraid of it," continued Teeter. "We can swim but are not the best of swimmers, not having the right kind of feet for that. But we are not helpless if, when flying over water, we have to come down on or in it."

"What is the difference?" Peter wanted to know.

"Difference between what?" asked Teeter. He looked puzzled.

"Between being on the water and in it. Aren't you in the water when you are on it? Your legs must be or you couldn't swim," said Peter.

"Don't be stupid, Peter Rabbit. When we are on the water we are mostly above it. When we are in the water we are in all over," retorted Teeter a bit impatiently.

131

"What do you mean by all over?" persisted Peter.

"Like this," said Teeter. He swam out a little way and disappeared under water. In a moment he bobbed up. "That is what I call being *in* the water," said he.

"You were in all right. I guess a lot of folks don't know that you can dive," replied Peter.

"It comes in handy sometimes. More than once I have escaped from a Hawk that way. Speaking of Hawks here comes Sharpshin again!" cried Teeter. He gave the hide signal to the four tiny Sandpipers on the shore and took to his wings, flying low over the water toward the other shore.

By this time Sharpshin was so close to him that Peter held his breath as he watched. Could Teeter get across in time? Even if he should what could he do to escape that fierce feathered hunter so close behind him? Peter had the unhappy feeling that he was about to see the end of an old friend. "He hasn't a chance," moaned Peter in his mind.

Sharpshin was now so close to Teeter that Peter could barely see between them. There was a little splash. Peter blinked. That Hawk was flying away with no one in his claws. A moment later Teeter bobbed up on the water. He had dived while in full flight. He returned to shore as if nothing had happened.

"A handy trick, isn't it?" said he, and chuckled at the look on Peter's face.

"That was wonderful!" cried Peter admiringly. "I had no

idea I ever would see you again. I guess that Hawk was as surprised as I was."

"It was nothing. Sharpshin wasn't surprised. He was disappointed but not surprised. He has had that happen more than once before. It is a nice trick when you know just how and just when to do it," said Teeter.

"True. Very true," agreed Peter gravely. "It always is nice to do something you know how to do if you know when to do it. The trouble with most folks is that if they know how they don't know when, and if they know when they don't know how. I guess if the hows and whens of life were always learned together we would all be better off. When you plunged under water what did you do? Did you dive to the bottom?"

"I flew along to where you saw me come up," replied Teeter in a matter-of-fact tone.

"You mean you swam," Peter corrected.

"I mean I flew. You may call it swimming but I call it flying," retorted the Sandpiper as if he thought that settled the matter.

"Do you mean that you used your wings?" asked Peter.

Teeter's reply was short and a bit testy. "How could I fly without using my wings? Tell me that, Peter Rabbit."

Peter remembered something. He remembered looking down from a high bank and seeing Dipper the Grebe using his wings under water. "You mean you swim with your wings the way Dipper does," said he.

Teeter nodded. "We call it flying, not swimming," said he.

133

"If you prefer to call it swimming go ahead. It won't prevent me from flying in the water as well as in the air. If you will go up on that high bank where you can look down in deep water I'll show you how I do it."

Of course Peter agreed at once. He hopped up on the high bank. It was the very place from which he had once watched Dipper the Grebe. The water was clear and still. Not a single Merry Little Breeze was around to ripple the surface. For a short distance out from the shore Peter could see to the bottom.

"Peet-weet! Watch me!" called Teeter. He flew out and right in front of Peter dived. Peter could see him plainly. Sure enough he was flying through the water. Anyway he was using his wings to drive him through the water.

"Well?" said he when he returned to the surface.

"I guess we'll call it flying. Anyway it looks like it. Do you know what I think? I think you are as much a water bird as a land bird," said Peter.

"No," replied Teeter, shaking his head. "I'm a shore bird who has found out that it is handy to be able to feel at home on and in the water."

"You seem to feel at home wherever you are, on the land, in the air or in the water," said Peter.

"I do. Why shouldn't I?" replied Teeter.

"It is wonderful, truly wonderful," murmured Peter, who is at home only on land, and he was right. It was wonderful.

Teeter began walking along with the water just over his toes. Now and then he picked up something to eat. At the place where he now was the bottom sloped away gently. He began to wade out. At first the water was just over his feet. Soon it was halfway up his legs. Then it was up to his body and as he picked about with his long bill his head was wholly under water.

"He'll be swimming in a minute," thought Peter.

You should have seen Peter's eyes a moment later. He was staring at Teeter as if never having seen him before. He never

had seen him as he was seeing him now. Teeter wasn't swimming. He wasn't using his wings. He was *running* along on the bottom. The water was shallow and Peter could see him plainly. In a moment he bobbed up for air. He couldn't hold his breath for long.

"You can't do that," cried Peter. Then he grinned. It still seemed an impossible thing for anyone who didn't live in the water to do. But Teeter had done it, and he hadn't been showing off either. It was plain that he didn't think he had done anything at all remarkable.

Later, at home in the dear Old Briar-patch, Peter told Mrs. Peter about the things he had seen Teeter do. "He is wonderful, that Teeter. I wish you could have seen him, my dear." There was respect, a great deal of respect, in Peter's voice.

Mrs. Peter looked at him queerly, but all she said was, "I hope there is nothing wrong with your eyes. You certainly have been seeing things."

Peter was looking across the Green Meadows toward the Smiling Pool. "He can fly, swim, dive and run under water," he murmured half aloud. Then he turned to look at Mrs. Peter. "And there is nothing the matter with my eyes," said he somewhat sharply.

XX. Something Wrong with Laughing Brook

A cause for everything exists;
It can be found if one persists.
— GRANDFATHER FROG

SOMETHING WAS THE MATTER in the Smiling Pool. Peter Rabbit felt it without knowing what it was that made things seem different. He had been over there only the evening before and then had noticed nothing unusual. But as soon as he had arrived this evening he had felt that something was wrong.

Jerry Muskrat took no notice of him, simply didn't seem to see him. He appeared to have something on his mind, to be worried. Grandfather Frog merely rolled his big goggly eyes up at Peter, then turned his back to gaze out over the Smiling Pool as if watching something. Spotty the Turtle had an anxious look. Nobody paid any attention to Peter. He didn't quite know what to make of it.

It was just the beginning of a warm evening near the end of summer, and still light. Peter had come over early. He could see all over the Smiling Pool. But like so many other folks Peter isn't observing. Often he doesn't really use his eyes. This was one of those times. The Smiling Pool seemed as always. Only the people living there seemed different. They appeared to be uneasy, as if they were worried. Peter couldn't understand it.

Jerry Muskrat climbed up on the roof of his house built in the water and wholly surrounded by it. Mrs. Jerry joined him. They began talking in their squeaky voices. The house was but a little way out from the bank and Peter was near enough to overhear them.

"It is still going down," squeaked Jerry.

"I know it," squeaked Mrs. Jerry. She sounded worried. "If it doesn't stop going down pretty soon we'll have to move over to our house in the bank. This one won't be safe."

Peter pricked up his ears. What was going on here? Why wouldn't that house be safe? He was just about to ask when

Grandfather Frog left his big lily pad and swam over to Jerry's house.

"What do you make of it?" croaked Grandfather Frog.

"I don't know what to make of it," squeaked Jerry. "There has been plenty of rain. There isn't any reason for it, no reason at all that I can see."

"Wrong," croaked Grandfather Frog. "There is a reason for everything. There always is. Never forget that."

"Then what is the reason for this?" squeaked Mrs. Jerry. Her voice was sharp.

"I don't know," croaked Grandfather Frog. "But I do know that there is a reason. There has to be. There always is."

"So you said before. That doesn't help any," squeaked Jerry.

Just then Mrs. Quack flew in from the Big River. She swam over near the others. "Well, well, what's going on here? What's the matter with the Smiling Pool?" she quacked.

"That is what we want to know. What *is* the matter with the Smiling Pool? Is anything different on the Big River?" squeaked Jerry.

Mrs. Quack shook her head. "Everything is the same over there excepting that the Big River is a little higher than it usually is at this time of year. That isn't surprising. You know there has been much rain lately," she quacked.

"We were just speaking of it when you arrived," said Grandfather Frog. "How can there be more and less at the same time?

139

Just tell me that. You say there is more in the Big River, but there certainly is less here in the Smiling Pool, and it is growing still less all the time."

Peter Rabbit couldn't keep still any longer. "Less of what?" he cried.

"Water," croaked Grandfather Frog. "Don't you see that for yourself, Longears? What is the matter with your eyes?"

Peter looked all around. Now he saw that there was a difference in the Smiling Pool. The Big Rock stood a little higher out of water. So did Jerry Muskrat's house. Grandfather Frog's big green lily pad seemed to be a little nearer the shore. Even the cattails seemed to be taller than they had been. Peter's eyes opened very wide. "Why, the water is going down!" he exclaimed.

"Do tell," replied Grandfather Frog testily. "But tell us why."

That the Smiling Pool was shrinking there was no doubt. Moreover it was shrinking fast. The water was going down and down and the banks were rising up and up. No wonder the little people living there were worried. It wasn't just the shrinking of the Smiling Pool that bothered them, but the mystery of it. They had seen the Smiling Pool shrink before but always had known the reason for it. It always shrinks when the weather is dry for a long time. In midsummer it always is smaller than in spring and late fall because there is less rain to keep it filled.

But of late there had been more rain than usual, so the water should be higher instead of lower.

The Smiling Pool continued to become smaller. The finny folk who live there had less and less room for swimming. What if it dried up altogether? What would they do then? What could they do? They couldn't even go down to the Big River, for Laughing Brook was drying up too.

Grandfather Frog and all the other Frogs were just as worried. They could and would go down in the mud of the bottom. They would soon be getting ready to do that for the winter anyway. But what if there should be no water at all and the mud should dry up! It was much the same with Spotty the Turtle and all the other Turtles.

Jerry Muskrat and Mrs. Jerry had to leave their fine house and move to their other house in the bank. You see water no longer surrounded that house in the Smiling Pool. There was water only on the side where it had been deepest. Reddy Fox or any other enemy could walk right out to that house and tear it open. No longer was it safe. So they had moved to their home in the bank with the entrance still under water. But they were beginning to worry about that. It had been in deep water, but now there was but little water above it and soon there would be none at all. What should they do then?

The cattails and rushes no longer had wet feet. They no longer stood in water, but in unsightly dried and drying mud. Where once Laughing Brook had poured into the upper part of the

Smiling Pool there was now only a narrow channel along which trickled a little water.

Laughing Brook had stopped laughing. Peter Rabbit had always loved the sound of Laughing Brook. Now there was no laughter, no happy gurgling, no merry chatter, only a strange silence. Laughing Brook had shrunk even more than the Smiling Pool. Indeed, there was no Laughing Brook, only a stony bed between banks, a little water trickling between the stones, and here and there little pools. In the deepest of these small fishes were crowded, much worse off than the worried finny folk in the Smiling Pool. In those small pools they were trapped with no chance for escape should Longlegs the Heron, or Rattles the Kingfisher, or any other hungry fisherman happen along.

Peter had started up Laughing Brook but didn't go far. He had to hurry back to tell his friends in the Smiling Pool what he had found out. Of course it wasn't news to them. They knew and had always known that the water of the Smiling Pool came from Laughing Brook and that whatever happened to the Smiling Pool would have to first happen to Laughing Brook. Peter hadn't thought of that.

He told Mrs. Peter all about it when he got home to the dear Old Briar-patch. "There isn't any Laughing Brook and soon there won't be any Smiling Pool," said he mournfully.

"Then perhaps you will stay at home more. I hope so anyway," said Mrs. Peter drily.

Peter twitched his wobbly little nose at her. "The Jerry Muskrats may have to move down to the Big River, and that will be just too bad," said he.

"Will it? I won't miss them," replied Mrs. Peter, who seldom leaves the dear Old Briar-patch.

XXI. The Borrowed Water

For self alone we cannot live;
We take and we must also give.

— PADDY THE BEAVER

NO MORE was there a Smiling Pool. To be sure there was a pool, but it wasn't much of a pool, not enough of a one to smile. In the same way there no longer was a brook that laughed, not down near what had been the Smiling Pool anyway, nor between that and the Big River. With less and less water in them the Smiling Pool had become little more than a puddle, and

Laughing Brook a trickle. And still the cause was a mystery to the little people who lived there.

Jerry and Mrs. Jerry Muskrat were in despair. They had been forced to leave their house in the Smiling Pool when it was no longer surrounded by water and so was no longer safe. Now they were no longer safe in the house in the bank to which they had moved. The entrance had been under water, but now it was above water, open to anyone who wanted to enter.

"We can't stay here," declared Jerry. "There is nothing for us to do but to go down to the Big River. Mrs. Quack says there is plenty of water there. I guess we should have gone before. Probably by now there isn't a puddle deep enough anywhere along the way to give us protection should Reddy Fox or Mrs. Reddy or a Dog happen to find us."

"I suppose we must," agreed Mrs. Jerry. "We aren't safe here and we won't be as long as there isn't water deep enough for us to dive in. Oh, dear! Here it is almost time for us to be making ready for winter and we haven't even a place to live and don't know where to look for one."

"Hush!" interrupted Jerry. "Someone is coming." He was looking toward the alders that grew at the edge of the small swamp through which Laughing Brook had made its way to the Smiling Pool.

Mrs. Jerry moved nearer to him and both watched the alders anxiously, ready to run or to fight if they must should an enemy appear. They were afraid as seldom had they been afraid before.

145

It wasn't cowardly fear. Muskrat folk are not cowardly. No one will fight with greater courage than will they. It was because they understood fully how slight was their chance to escape should an enemy bigger than themselves come out of those alders. Never had they so realized how important, how terribly important to them, plenty of water, deep water, could be.

Out from the alders walked a stranger. Another followed him. Side by side they sat up the better to look around. The two Muskrats stared at their visitors unbelievingly. Was something the matter with their eyes? There must be. Whoever had heard of giant Muskrats? Certainly they never had. Yet that is what these strangers looked like at the first startled glance.

Now the strangers saw them and one of them grinned good-naturedly. "Oh, my goodness, look at those teeth!" exclaimed Mrs. Jerry in a whisper, and shivered.

It is hardly to be wondered at that she shivered. The front teeth, the cutting teeth, were so long and big that the lips were not wholly closed over them. Instead of being white they were a bright orange. They looked dangerous. Yes, sir, they looked very dangerous indeed. They looked as if they might take a leg off with a single bite.

Then she caught sight of the tails of their visitors. Her eyes opened wider than ever. "Whoever heard of tails like those?" she whispered. "They are flat the wrong way."

A Muskrat's tail is, as you know, flattened on the sides. It is of good length and comparatively narrow. The big tails Mrs.

146

Jerry was staring at were flattened top and bottom. They were quite thick and very broad, paddle shape.

Jerry's face cleared when he saw those tails. "Don't be afraid," he whispered. "Those are Beaver folk. Once a long time ago I went far up Laughing Brook to a pond of Paddy the Beaver. You know some folks call Paddy our big cousin. He isn't really because we belong to different families, but except for size we do look something alike, and we do live in much the same way. I wonder what these two are doing way down here."

"It won't do any harm to ask," whispered Mrs. Jerry.

"Are you Paddy the Beaver?" squeaked Jerry in his politest manner, turning to one of the strangers.

The visitor grunted and his great orange teeth seemed to fill his whole mouth. "No," said he. "I am one of his children. They call me Slaptail. This is Mrs. Slaptail. Do you live here?"

"We did, but we can't any longer. We are just about to go down to the Big River," replied Jerry.

"Why?" asked Slaptail.

"Can't you see for yourself? There isn't water enough," spoke up Mrs. Jerry. Her squeaky voice was sharp.

"The water has been growing less and less for days, why we don't know. Soon there won't be any at all. To live safely we must have plenty of water. So now, at the very time we should be getting ready for winter, we must go look for a place where we can make a new home," explained Jerry.

Slaptail looked at Mrs. Slaptail, then back at Jerry. "Things

147

may not be as bad as they seem. Perhaps in a little while there will be plenty of water here again," said he.

"I wish we could think so. But we don't know why the water stopped coming down Laughing Brook, so we know no reason why it should run again," said Jerry.

Again Slaptail looked at Mrs. Slaptail. She nodded. "We do," said he.

Mrs. Jerry looked at him quickly. "What do you mean by that?" she squeaked.

Slaptail showed all his great teeth in what he intended for a friendly grin. "We know why the water stopped running and why it will run again before long," said he.

The two Muskrats stared at him. "How do you know?" squeaked Jerry.

Slaptail turned to Mrs. Slaptail. "Shall I tell him?" he asked.

"Why not?" she replied.

"We stopped the water," said Slaptail in the most matter-of-fact tone. "Of course we didn't know you were living down here," he added.

"Not that that would have made any difference. We had to do it," said Mrs. Slaptail.

"Why? I don't see why," squeaked Jerry. He sounded angry.

"We needed a new pond. We had to have a new pond. The only way we could get one was to have Laughing Brook make it for us," explained Slaptail as if it were such a simple matter that everyone should understand it.

148

"So we built a dam across Laughing Brook to hold the water back. And when our pond is big enough, which will be soon now, we will let Laughing Brook run down here again and fill up this place, whatever you call it," said Mrs. Slaptail.

"We did call it the Smiling Pool, but it isn't much of a pool now and it doesn't smile any more," said Mrs. Jerry sadly.

"It will," promised Slaptail. "It will be as smiling as ever it was."

"You had no right to take the water away from us," squeaked Jerry indignantly.

"I'm sorry we inconvenienced you, but we had to do it. We Beavers live on the bark of certain kinds of trees. To get it we have to cut down the trees and then cut them into logs that we can handle. There must be water near enough for us to get those logs into it without too much difficulty and then float them to our food pile near our house in the pond where we live. We had cut all the food trees near that pond, so we had to make another pond near other food trees not too far away. We didn't steal the water; we just borrowed it," explained Slaptail.

"Borrowed it!" exclaimed Jerry.

"Borrowed it," repeated Slaptail. "In a few days you'll have it back. That pond will be big enough and Laughing Brook will be on its way to the Big River again. We were going down there ourselves just to see what it is like, but if it is like this all the way I think we will go back home. Remember that the water is only borrowed, and stop worrying."

The two Beavers turned and disappeared in the alders. The very next day Laughing Brook began to gurgle. Two days later it was laughing and the Smiling Pool had filled enough to begin to smile. In a week it was its own smiling self.

And once more all the way from the Great Mountain until it loses itself in the Big River there was rejoicing and happiness along Laughing Brook.

THE END